HOMOEOF

WHAT ARE WE SWALI

STEVEN RANSOM

Credence Publications

Homoeopathy - What Are We Swallowing?

First published in 1999
by Credence Publications

ISBN 0-9535012-2-1
10 9 8 7 6 5 4 3 2

Printed and bound in Great Britain by

Credence Publications
PO Box 15
Uckfield
East Sussex, TN22 3WX
England

Table of Contents

Acknowledgements

I would like to thank my darling wife for her patience and good humour over these last nine years and for her editorial skills. Many thanks also to Phillip for appearing from nowhere to rescue the book so wonderfully; and to Manchester Central Library …for simply being there for me!

A Straight Stick

There is a great deal of interest today in alternative therapies, the body, mind, spirit approach to health and well-being known as holism (*holos* - Greek for 'whole'). All the therapies have high media profile and a large number of holistic books and magazines are now widely read. A 1995 market intelligence report stated:

"The alternative medicines market was estimated to be worth £62.7 million in 1994, which represents an increase in sales of some 23% since 1992, making it one of the fastest growing consumer healthcare markets [1]."

A more recent MORI poll reported 46% of 1000 people would be happy to try some form of alternative therapy [2]. And today, with the year 2000 now less than twelve months away, the therapies appear to be more popular than ever. Without doubt, holism has arrived in this country in a big way.

Considering the influence and stature of alternative therapies, and considering also that they have a direct interest in our most precious asset - our health - it is surprising how little is generally known about this major contributor to health care. It wouldn't be unfair or condescending to pool the general perceptions of alternative therapies and paraphrase them thus:

"A fairly recent thing, all about natural remedies and therapies, a lot of different people with a lot of different approaches, all helping us to feel and get better, naturally."

---

[1] **Mintel** *Complementary **Medicines**, May 1995
[2] Health & Fitness Magazine, April 1995

The general consensus of opinion is that alternative therapies are basically good, and that, in the main, they are a valid addition to 20th century western healthcare.

This book is the result of nine years research into alternative therapies, and into one therapy in particular - homoeopathy - arguably the most popular and respected alternative healthcare treatment in this country today. As with many of these therapies, the inner workings of homoeopathy seem to be shrouded in mystery and intrigue. Over the years a number of different theories have been put forward in an attempt to explain homoeopathy's healing powers, but to date there is still very little agreement on how homoeopathic remedies are actually supposed to work. Homoeopathy remains a sort of magical medicine.

This book sets out to demystify the myth, mystery and magic of homoeopathy. Unearthed for the reader are some little publicised but undeniable and sometimes quite unsavoury truths concerning the history, theory and practice of homoeopathy. I believe that making these truths public knowledge will lay this multi-million pound industry wide open to quite justifiable charges of deception and unethical practice. And as this story unfolds, we shall see that deception and unethical practice are by no means confined to the practice of homoeopathy.

Questioning the claims of homoeopathy and of alternative therapies in general is by association, questioning a great wealth of well-documented positive personal experiences and brings into question what many people believe to be *"...the overwhelming evidence which shows that these therapies actually work!"* On the face of it these arguments appear quite reasonable, but they do need to be examined a little more carefully. Doing so at this early stage will help to set 'feelings', 'personal experience' and 'overwhelming evidence' into some sort of context.

Wealth of Personal Experience

Whilst feelings and personal experience can sometimes play a valuable role in leading us to the truth of a matter, the inescapable reality that our senses often deceive us is acknowledged and accounted for in all fields of sensible enquiry, not just medicine. The history of discovery and invention, with all its triumphs, false trails and by-ways contains many graphic examples of just how wrong we can be when we allow feelings and experience to be our guide.

It was Galileo who said, *"Look, I've done some calculations - the earth isn't stationary, we actually revolve around the sun."* To everyone else at the time, this appeared a most illogical statement to make:

"If the earth revolves, then how come there isn't a constant wind blowing in our faces? Surely the clouds would pass us by in just one direction!"

"A ball thrown straight up in the air comes straight back down. If the earth revolves, how come the ball doesn't land a little to the left or to the right?"

"Everyone knows we're the centre of the universe. Let him recant or lock him up!"

These arguments and more, appeared irrefutable, all of them drawn from our everyday personal experience. Galileo was locked up. He eventually recanted (though legend has it that as he did so, he was heard to mutter *"...and yet we move"*). We now know that Galileo was absolutely right and we were all absolutely wrong. I use the word we, because the tendency to rely on personal experience to measure right and wrong is deeply ingrained in us all. Highlighting this very real human weakness and bringing it into the context of this debate, the message to anyone with positive personal experience of homoeopathy is this: what can appear valid and healthy isn't necessarily so. We *can* be deceived.

Overwhelming Evidence

Information on alternative health is everywhere. There are innumerable specialist titles available and the majority of popular magazines and papers now have regular advice columns and/or articles on the therapies, especially homoeopathy. The influence the media is having on our perception of the therapies in general cannot be over-estimated and it is important that a few minutes is spent bringing 'overwhelming evidence' into its rightful context.

Our information-oriented society is showing increasing signs of owning a licence to print and transmit anything with little or no attention paid to accuracy or truth. The growing concern only now being shown over the easy access to uncensored and inaccurate information on the Internet is a prime example of attempting to close the door on an empty stable. Sadly, there is the same lack of concern being shown towards the majority of reporting on alternative health.

The popular press has very good reason to promote the therapies (nothing sells like the cover that reads **"Ten Ways to De-Stress Naturally!"**), but in all this promotional activity, very little attention is actually given to employing editors or researchers suitably qualified to recognise misleading and sometimes completely false information. The majority of media research files on homoeopathy, or any of the major therapies for that matter, invariably contain snippets from other books, magazines and supplements, most of the snippets unsourced, but all *apparently* correct.

Varro Tyler, the world-respected professor of plant medicine, offers us this sobering summary of another of today's popular therapies - that of herbalism:

"For whatever reason, be it misguided belief, personal gain or simply ignorance, pseudoherbalists have flooded the market with literature containing so much outdated and downright inaccurate information about the use of herbs, that interested individuals, lay or professional, who approach this field for the very first time, become totally confused[3]*."*

The inevitable result of this lax reporting chain is an enormous amount of disinformation in constant circulation, very much influencing our perception of alternative therapies today.

In his book *The Psychology of Perception*, M D Vernon writes:

"Recent experimental investigation has shown that change and variation of stimulation are essential to maintain the efficiency of perception, and of the cognitive processes associated with it. If people are exposed to artificial conditions in which stimulation remains unvarying over a period of time, perception may even cease to function[4]*."*

There is no variation in the news on homoeopathy. As with all the therapies, the picture never changes. On a daily basis the news is positively healthy. Where is that different perspective that might bring the necessary variation to stimulate alertness and help draw attention to some less than healthy features of homoeopathy? Ask yourself when was the last time you read

---

[3] **Tyler, Varro** Pharmaceutical Products Press 1994
[4] **Vernon, M D** *Psychology of Perception*, Penguin 1977

anything that seriously questioned the validity of *any* of the therapies? With no frame of reference available to help us plot our true position, we are in fact adrift, seemingly unperturbed in a vast ocean of unvarying good news.

In illustrating the term 'frame of reference', I like the simple analogy of the straight stick used by the speaker D L Moody, who said:

"The best way to decide whether a stick is crooked or not, is not to spend time arguing over the matter, but simply to lay a straight stick beside it."

We need a straight stick to measure the therapies. People are now spending large amounts of time and money on them, especially homoeopathy. This book has been written to give people what should be their right - informed choice. To date, informed choice is most definitely not what the consumer has been given, as we shall soon discover.

If you're using or contemplating using homoeopathy, and you have a few nagging questions that you want straight answers to, then this book is for you. If you're using or contemplating using any of the therapies for that matter, and you would like a few guidelines on how to begin assessing their claims, then this also is the book for you. Whilst the therapies may vary outwardly (needles, crystals, flowers or herbs, etc.), we shall see that despite these differences, they all share the same worrying fundamental rules of play. If your thing is the *'outing'* of high-level corporate trickery, with plenty of plot and intrigue along the way, then you're in for a treat here!

Whatever your inclination, I hope this book will serve you as that straight stick.

"Mr. Lely, I desire you would use all your skill to paint my picture truly like me, and to flatter me not at all. Remark all these roughnesses, pimples, warts and everything as you see me, otherwise I will never pay a farthing for it [5]."

Oliver Cromwell

The Founder of Homoeopathy

While there are a whole host of therapies out there which warrant detailed examination, let us begin this study of alternative health by concentrating on homoeopathy. It has a very interesting history, and serves as a good subject by which to demonstrate some very commonly shared principles. Included below are some brief extracts taken from a broad range of popular books on the subject. These texts will serve to illustrate the typical picture we are given regarding the history, founding principles and general benefits of homoeopathy.

"Samuel Hahnemann, the remarkable genius who discovered, developed and systematised the fundamental laws of cure that are producing such revolutionary changes in thinking about health and disease [6]."
George Vithoulkas - Science of Homoeopathy

"Basing his remedies on the 'like cures like' principle, Hahnemann found he could produce efficient remedies by greatly diluting substances which in a large dose would have created symptoms similar to those seen in the patient.

---

[5] *Great Guides & Illustrations*, Word Publishers 1988
[6] **Vithoulkas, George** *The Science of Homoeopathy*, Thorsons 1986

Hahnemann had finally arrived at his goal - an alternative form of treatment that was both effective and safe [7]."

Homoeopathy Family Handbook (BHA recommended)

"Samuel Hahnemann not only discovered a new approach to the healing of the sick, which he called homoeopathy, but he also gave humanity a method of curing illness which since the end of his life, has grown slowly, gently and permanently to every continent on earth, and in its time has given back to millions of people the health and well-being which they sought. It is my belief homoeopathy will find its true place at the forefront of medicine in the twenty-first century [8]."

Peter Finigan - The Natural Therapies A-Z

These texts may well serve as flattering portraits, but do they really capture a true likeness of the subject? That question is left for you to decide as we begin at the beginning of the story of homoeopathy.

The Early Years

Samuel Hahnemann, the founder of homoeopathy, was born in Meissen, Germany in 1755. Hahnemann's father worked in the Meissen porcelain factory and took an active interest in his son's education, encouraging him towards serious study from a very early age. This recollection from an acquaintance of Hahnemann's father gives us some idea of his methods of encouragement.

"Hahnemann's father, before going to the factory, used frequently to lock his son in a room, close the shutters and give him a difficult sentence to ponder over, of which he had to give

---

[7] *Homoeopathy Family Handbook*, Thorsons 1986
[8] **Finigan, Peter** *The Natural Therapies A-Z*, Thorsons 1994

an account on his father's return. This contributed to making his son an original thinker[9]."

At twelve, young Samuel could read and write Greek and had begun to teach the subject at his school. Samuel stayed at Princes School, until his father, desirous of extra income into their hard-up household, ordered that he leave school at sixteen and start to earn a living. His father found him a position working in a local grocery store. Samuel stayed only a very short time before walking out. It was Samuel's mother who came to the rescue, hiding her boy away for several days, whilst she talked her husband round from his great wrath at Samuel's desertion.

The school, recognising young Hahnemann's exceptional intelligence, offered him a place free of charge on the understanding that he continued to teach Greek, an offer Mr Hahnemann senior finally allowed his son to accept. At twenty, Samuel Hahnemann left Princes School, fluent in five languages and with a strong desire to study medicine. Concerning Hahnemann's early years, one of his tutors wrote:

"Already in the tender years of youth, Hahnemann was obliged to work for his maintenance and education. A happy, carefree youth was entirely denied him and from early days he was constrained to unceasing work[10]."

With very little money, young Hahnemann left home for Leipzig University to study medicine. He was now on his own and apart from the odd letter to his mother, there is no record in any biographies which indicate that Hahnemann ever returned home. Hahnemann stayed at Leipzig for two years and then moved to Vienna, continuing his medical studies at a local

---

[9] **Haehl, Richard** *Samuel Hahnemann - His Life and Work*, Jain Publishers 1971
[10] Haehl, Richard, ibid.

hospital. In order to fund his studies, Hahnemann tried to earn some money by translation work, but found it very difficult to make ends meet.

Almost at starvation point, he was introduced to an exceedingly wealthy man, Samuel Brukenthal, the governor of Transylvania (now Romania). Impressed with Hahnemann's keen mind, Brukenthal invited him to become his personal librarian. Hahnemann immediately accepted the post and, putting his medical studies on hold, set out on the arduous seven-hundred mile journey to Hermannstadt, Brukenthal's Transylvanian home town high up in the Carpathian Mountains.

Aside from being extremely rich, Brukenthal also held the position of Master of the Chair at the Madgeburg Freemasons' Lodge and he opened the door for Hahnemann to become a Mason at the Lodge St Andreas zu den drei Seeblattern in Hermannstadt. Hahnemann's admittance into the Lodge took place in October 1777.

Very few of Hahnemann's biographers pay attention to this period of his life, a period that must not be overlooked. In order to gain insight into this extraordinary movement and its influence on the young Hahnemann, the following brief history of European Freemasonry is included.

Freemasonry in Hahnemann's Day

The beginnings of European Masonic activity can be traced back to the late 1720's, with fledgling Lodges appearing across France under the direct control of what became known as the English Mother Lodge system. The Mother Lodges of this period comprised mainly of wealthy and influential individuals from privileged society - certain royals, philosophers, politicians, scientists and writers.

Aside from the opportunity for networking and conviviality, the purpose of the Lodge meeting was to impart knowledge, supposedly hidden from the masses but considered necessary for the advancement of mankind. Through secret ritual and instruction, Lodge members were *'enlightened'* by degrees, and when instructed with sufficient secret knowledge, it was believed the now *'illumined'* brethren could begin the process of transforming society, operating within their own particular sphere of influence.

Supporters of Freemasonry described Lodge meetings as a means of conveying to the individual the upright principles of brotherly love, equality and truth. Opposition to Freemasonry stemmed from the fact that Masonic rituals and teachings demonstrated occult influence and that meetings were always conducted behind closed doors, inviting the very reasonable question - why should knowledge considered beneficial to mankind be kept from the great majority of mankind?

As more and more Lodges appeared across Europe, so too did numerous men of mystery. Considered to be custodians of secret doctrines, these *'Masonic adepts'* travelled the length and breadth of Europe, instructing Lodges in such matters as alchemy, spiritual chemistry, magical sciences, spiritism and cabalistic knowledge.

Cagliostro was one such mystery man, whose particular style of ritual is avidly described as follows:

"After an elaborate preamble -which included invocations of the planetary spirits - the 'Dove of the Rite' - a young boy or girl was hypnotized and put into a state of alleged clairvoyance, in which she would prophesy, see visions and pronounce upon the candidate's fitness. All this while Cagliostro carried out ceremonies of ritual magic [11]."

These extravagant ceremonies proved very popular and Lodges performing such rites flourished across Europe. Pasqually was another instructor, teaching the secrets of liberating the soul in order to unite fellow brethren with the Divine. Using cabalistic chant and invocation, the initiate was permitted to *'see'* his guardian angel and also *'the Repairer of souls of all intelligent beings on Earth and throughout the Universe [12].'*

Ceremonies promising visible manifestations of spirit essence were always well attended. The desire to commune with the higher realms paved the way for many charlatans, dubious adventurers and masters of illusion skilled in the art of recreating luminescent apparitions and ethereal shimmerings. Quite regularly mirrors and other such optical instruments were used to great effect. These methods were by no means new. The Aesculapian healing temples of some two thousand years earlier were noted for their *'piped'* angelic choirs and the very earthly looking *'gods'* who hovered mysteriously at the bedside of the fee-paying sick.

---

[11] **Hamill, John & R A Gilbert** *World Freemasonry*, Aquarian Press 1991
[12] Hamill, John, ibid.

Of particular interest to this study is the influence of Johann Starck. A fervent alchemist and teacher of dark arts, Starck was heralded in Masonic circles as the absolute master in the art of spiritual transmutation - the regeneration of man. According to Starck, his recently acquired secret knowledge was originally revealed centuries earlier to a Hugo Von Paganis. Whilst sheltering in a cave, Von Paganis was apparently visited by seven wise men from the east. According to Von Paganis, such was the nature of the secret knowledge these *'seven wise men'* shared with him, that the cave was filled with a *'heavenly glow'*. The ancient documents now in Starck's possession were said to contain secret instruction on purifying the spiritual essence of man and separating it from his terrestrial nature. The following extract gives some idea of Starck's rites, which again proved very popular and were performed right across Europe.

"The initiate was instructed that in order to attain wisdom, art and virtue, it was necessary to honour the Supreme Being, to love the Brethren and all Mankind; to be temperate, courageous, steadfast in misfortune, humble and not to fear death. An oath was taken, his eyes were unbandaged, and his gaze directed towards a star of eighty-one lamps, flaming over the head of the presiding master. The knight was then allowed to have a glimpse of light through a half-opened door leading to The Temple of Secret Doctrine [13]*."*

Throughout the rite, much reference is made to alchemic symbolism and hidden meaning in numbers. Progressing onwards, thanks is given to The Architect of the Universe, The Supreme Being, The Almighty, The Wise and all the while various doctrines are imparted....

---

[13] **Telepnef, Boris** *The Spiritual Masonry of Johann Starck,* Quatuor Coronati Lodge 2076 (Vol. 41) 1928

"We alone possess the knowledge, how to prepare from the four powers contained in Creation, the Primary Matter and then the Great Medicine for health and riches [14]."

Of necessity, this is a very condensed account of 18th century European Masonry but it affords some insight into the bizarre nature of the Lodge and brings greater understanding to the fleeting passages in those biographies that mention Hahnemann's Masonic connections. Biographer Richard Haehl hints at the extent of Hahnemann's involvement in the Lodge, the period in question italicised in bold in this text:

"From his school days onwards he had followed Descartes, Spinoza and Leibnitz - and then proceeded to vitalism and to the naturalism of Schelling and Hegel. ***He advanced beyond this to spiritism and for a while lost his way in occultism*** *[15]."* [emphasis mine]

Thomas Bradford's less guarded account of Hahnemann's time spent in the service of the Master of the Chair, Herr Brukenthal, now becomes much clearer:

"He carefully catalogued Baron Brukenthal's immense library of books and rare manuscripts. It was in these quiet, scholarly days that Hahnemann acquired that extensive and diverse knowledge of ancient literature and of occult sciences, of which he afterwards proved himself to be a master and with which he astonished the scientific world [16]."

Hahnemann stayed in Hermannstadt for nearly two years, immersing himself in all these strange teachings. Then, with enough money saved to continue his medical studies, he left

---

[14] Telepnef, Boris, ibid.
[15] Haehl, Richard, ibid.
[16] **Bradford, Thomas** *Life and Letters of Samuel Hahnemann*, Jain Publishers 1921

Transylvania and returned to Germany to finish his doctor's degree, finally granted to him in 1779 at the age of twenty-four.

What did a doctor's degree actually equate to in those days? Richard Haehl gives us some idea of late 18th century medicine.

"Truly the medical education such as was customary and possible to obtain at the end of the eighteenth century left much to be desired in extent and depth. Above all, when it is considered that universities like Leipzig had no hospital or clinic of their own, the practical training of the young medical students was extremely deficient. Students were crammed with theories and systems and then, after a few terms, were let loose on suffering humanity, there to win experience, knowledge and skills for themselves [17]."

It is appropriate at this point to spend a few minutes looking at health and health care in Hahnemann's time. Doing so will help us fully appreciate his much publicised and quite understandable revulsion towards the medical practice of the day.

---

[17] Haehl, Richard, ibid.

Medical Practice in Hahnemann's Era

Germany was no different to any other country in Europe regarding medicine and health in the late 18th century. Conditions were appalling. There was little or no town planning, living conditions were cramped and there were no sewerage facilities. Pulling the flush entailed shouting a warning from your window (first or fifth floor, it didn't really matter) and throwing the contents of the slop bucket into the street below. It wasn't unusual for these very unhygienic streets to be busy with locals buying food and produce which would be on open display. In poorer sections of the community, children would often be stitched into their clothes for the winter. The infant mortality rate was understandably high.

The Physician
If you were rich, you could afford the services of the physician. His medical bag consisted of sharp knives for the letting of copious amounts of blood, leeches to suck equally copious amounts of blood, various instruments for the removal of limbs, one or two powerful crude opiates for reducing pain, no disinfectant, and even less by way of bedside manner. For these services the hapless patient was charged. Some shrewd doctors would endeavour to keep relatives in the operating room and those who fainted at the sight of the doctor at work would incur a modest fee for *'being revived'*. It is no exaggeration to say that patients regularly died of their physician!

The Quack
If you had little money, there was always the quack, the rogue and the vagabond healer, on hand and able to cure anything! The quack's remedies included crab-claw, grease from a hanged man's scalp, live toads, earthworms, goose dung, powdered bones, boiled fox; in fact anything that could be boiled, crunched

up, powdered and swallowed was available as a medicine from someone, somewhere. These extravagant remedies were matched only by the extravagant claims that supported them.

One ingenious gentleman set up shop promoting a cure for diseases *'as yet unknown to mankind but lethal.'* These diseases included moonfall, hockogrockle, wambling trot, marthambles and the strong fives. Remarkably those who took the remedies never contracted any of these diseases, the old fraudster making a tidy sum in the process!

Vanity was well catered for with long queues at the doors of those who could preserve beauty and cease ageing. There was an exceptionally long queue at the door of the Count de St Germaine, an itinerant quack who, at aged sixty (but looking twenty-five years younger), had a roguish flash of inspiration, inventing his own elixir for everlasting life (another to add to history's long list). Hiring a horse and carriage and an accomplice in the guise of a man-servant, he dressed himself in the finest clothes and travelled Europe with his elixirs claiming to be two thousand years old.

Throughout his very lucrative itinerary, jewel-encrusted audiences would listen enthralled as the Count relived his conversations with the rich and famous down through history, such as Hannibal, Alfred the Great and Nero. His fanciful narrative would be interrupted only as he paused to take one or two delicate sips from an ornate hip-flask containing his sparkling elixir. After a spellbinding evening's entertainment, the artful raconteur would lead his audiences *en masse* to his awaiting carriage from where he would briskly dispense the precious *'aqua vitae'*.

On one occasion the Count's manservant was cross-examined over his master's early travels in Palestine and a supposedly unforgettable evening spent in the company of Richard Ist. In a commendable defence of his master's tale, the manservant confessed he could not verify the finer details, having been in the Count's service for only the last five hundred years! Horace Walpole, the 18th century writer and historian, had the pleasure of meeting the Count. He remarked in one of his diaries:

"He sings and plays on the violin wonderfully, but he is not very sensible [18]*."*

To summarise, the discovery of microbiological disease was still some way off, and it was only at the very end of the 18th century that Edward Jenner would further Lady Montague's discovery of crude inoculation and go on to alleviate much suffering through vaccination. In short, there was very little good medicine to brighten the dark backdrop of widespread chicanery, fraud, inadvertent poisoning, bloody maiming and not a little death - all in the name of doctoring. Medical historian Oliver Wendell Holmes said of the medicine of the period:

"If the whole pharmacopoeia were thrown into the sea it would be better for mankind and worse for the fishes."

---

[18] **Constable, Nick** *Fated Destiny*, Blitz Editions 1994

Dr Hahnemann Let Loose

It was into these conditions that Dr Samuel Hahnemann was *"...let loose on suffering humanity to win experience, knowledge and skill for himself."* As much as the prevailing medical conditions appalled him, Hahnemann was not immune from the temptation to elicit money by fraudulent means. Scarlet fever was a terrible scourge, killing literally hundreds of children. In the midst of one such epidemic, Hahnemann wrote a book which he said contained a number of helpful secrets including *"...one of the most beneficial discoveries ever made, an infallible remedy for the prevention and cure of scarlet fever [19]."*

Medical authorities at the time were aghast that Hahnemann might be in possession of a cure for this decimating disease, and was purposely withholding it for financial gain. Hahnemann retorted:

"It is making an appeal to my conscience that scarlet fever is raging and many hundreds of children are carried away by it ... but I cannot for the present publish my book without financial embarrassment. However, everyone who deposits a Freidrich D'or, as a subscription to my book, will receive a little powder free of charge, which contains enough to render several thousand people immune from scarlet fever [20]."

The remedy carried very complicated instructions which Hahnemann warned must be followed to the letter or the remedy would not work. Astonishment at Hahnemann's audacity turned to absolute rage when it was discovered that these very difficult instructions meant dissolving a tiny amount of crushed Belladonna into two million, four hundred thousand drops of water.

---

[19] Haehl, Richard, ibid.
[20] Haehl, Richard, ibid.

The remedy was of course absolutely ineffective. Scarlet fever continued to kill many hundreds of children, and the resulting furore forced Hahnemann to leave town. Belladonna (deadly nightshade) in any dilution plays no part whatsoever in the prevention or cure of scarlet fever. In fact there is still no cure for scarlet fever, although outbreaks of this disease have been greatly reduced by much healthier and less crowded living conditions.

Hahnemann then went on to *'discover'* a new alkaline salt, a discovery which aroused considerable interest amongst chemists at that time. This salt could be obtained from Hahnemann for the equivalent of £15.00 per lb. When it came to light that this new alkaline salt was in fact common salt costing 5p for the equivalent amount, Hahnemann replied, *"To err is human..."* and later stated, *"I am incapable of wilfully deceiving. However... I may, like other men, be unintentionally mistaken."*

After one incident in particular in which Hahnemann was alleged to have grossly overcharged an epileptic for a very unsuccessful course of treatment, the court physician of Brunswick, where Hahnemann was temporarily residing, was moved to write the following:

"I have now been fifty-seven years a medical practitioner in Brunswick but never have I known a local physician who was so avaricious and who practised so much charlatanism as Dr Hahnemann when residing in our city and later on in Königslutter. But because this kind of practice did not succeed in our country and also because the physicians were not allowed to dispense their own medicines, or to extract money out of patients' pockets by so called Arkana or secret remedies,

Hahnemann took up his staff and wandered on, and I do not know where he went to [21]."

Hahnemann's very questionable 'secret' remedies, his antagonistic and outspoken attitude towards his peers, publicly denouncing them as *'high-titled ravagers of health',* and his refusal to practice the medicine of the day incurred wrath and rejection wherever he went. In the twenty-four year period following his becoming a doctor, Hahnemann was forced to move no less than eighteen times.

There has been no need to resort to unfair character assassination to discover that the rosy glow in which Hahnemann is so often portrayed is actually very misleading. It is important we have a clear understanding of this period in his life, because it was during this time that Hahnemann was mulling over a whole range of ideas, some of which would go on to become the therapy we know today as homoeopathy. It was in his one-roomed accommodation with his wife and by now five children, that Hahnemann would sit reflecting on everyone else's failings and false medical doctrines when, in a flash of inspiration, he received what he believed to be the inklings of a divine calling to discover a new way forward.

"What a shameful, blasphemous thought! - I clasped my brow - that the wisdom of the Infinite Spirit animating the universe should not be able to create a means to pacify the sufferings of diseases which He after all had allowed to arise! ...would He leave no way open to the genius of mankind, otherwise so infallible, no easy, certain and dependable way of regarding disease correctly? [22]"

---

[21] Haehl, Richard, ibid.
[22] Haehl, Richard, ibid.

And sure enough it wasn't long before he, Christian Friedrich Samuel Hahnemann, announced to the world a healing art, a new medicine, homoeopathy, which he went on to describe as *"…the good which the Supreme Being permitted me to discover, or may I say, revealed to me, for the alleviation of the suffering of mankind* [23]*."*

Hahnemann was convinced he had been divinely called to discover a new way. Any study of medical practice of that time shows just how desperately a new way was needed. Let us now examine the route Hahnemann took to arrive at his discovery of homoeopathy.

---

[23] Haehl, Richard, ibid.

The Birth of Homoeopathy

In 1790, a publishing house sent Hahnemann a manuscript for translation. It was a treatise on the medicinal effects of cinchona bark, a remedy that was actually used very successfully in powdered form to combat the quartains or marsh fever, the debilitating illness we know as malaria. In this manuscript, a Dr Cullen had written that cinchona cured fever because of its astringent properties and its effect on the stomach. Hahnemann got to this paragraph in the chapter and, putting his pen down, he pondered on this statement, remarking quite rightly that there were much more powerful astringents than cinchona which, when taken, had no effect whatsoever on fever. He concluded that cinchona must cure fever some other way. Hahnemann decided to investigate for himself and conducted a simple experiment.

"I took for several days as an experiment, four drams of good cinchona twice daily. My feet and fingertips, etc., at first became cold. I became languid and drowsy, then my heart began to palpitate; my pulse became hard and quick, an intolerable anxiety and trembling but without a rigor; prostration in all the limbs; then pulsation in the head; redness in the cheeks; thirst. To sum up, all the symptoms typical of fever made their appearance. These paroxysms lasted from two to three hours every time I repeated the dose, and not otherwise [24]."

Hahnemann came to the conclusion that cinchona cured fever because it appeared to produce in him symptoms of fever. As an introduction to the first edition of his book on homoeopathy, Hahnemann wrote:

---

[24] Haehl, Richard, ibid.

"To obtain a quick and lasting cure, choose for every attack of illness a medicine which can produce a similar malady to the one it is to cure .... 'simila similibus curentur'... like cures like [25]."

Hahnemann announced that 'like cures like' was the new way forward.

As we have already seen, medical conditions were dire and Hahnemann was by no means alone in his distaste for much of the practice of the day. His startling news that he had discovered a new way forward without the bloodletting and leeches was welcome news indeed and his claims aroused considerable interest. Hahnemann's peers attempted to validate his claim that cinchona produced symptoms similar to malaria, and that it cured fever according to 'like cures like'.

Concerning the validation of scientific claims, Geoff Watts, author of *Pleasing the Patient*, makes this very good point.

"Researchers are required not only to publish their findings, but also to describe their method in sufficient detail to allow others to repeat the work. Indeed the repeatability of an experiment is one of the criteria by which scientists judge the claims of their peers [26]."

Although the medical practice of the late 18th century was very basic, the approach to the gathering of knowledge, as outlined by Geoff Watts, had been in existence in scientific circles long before Hahnemann's era. When Hahnemann's peers did test cinchona on themselves, they found that no one could reproduce the symptoms of fever Hahnemann claimed he had experienced. Incredibly, to this day no one has been able independently to repeat Hahnemann's cinchona experiment, the

---

[25] **Hahnemann, Christian Samuel** *Organon of Medicine*, Gollancz 1986
[26] **Watts, Geoff** *Pleasing the Patient*, Faber & Faber 1992

experiment that shaped the first principle of homoeopathy.

In today's books on the subject, there are many testimonies as to the brilliance of Hahnemann's experiments, but no mention at all is made of the fact that no one has yet been able to repeat them. Neither do today's authors draw attention to the many publications which summarily rejected Hahnemann's claims when first they were made. A Dr Schwartz of the Board of Health wrote at the time:

"Cinchona, even in the preparation advocated by Hahnemann, did not cause fever in either healthy people or animals [27]*."*

Hahnemann refused to enter into any kind of debate. He had his theory and he was sticking to it. Cullen also refused to be shifted, holding fast to his astringency argument. A number of other physicians at the time had each put forward different theories on cinchona's healing principles. The problem was, no one was able sensibly to advance any of their claims beyond mere personal opinion. Cinchona very obviously did cure fever.... but how?

The true answer did not become known for another thirty years. It was in 1820 that French chemist Joseph Pelletier isolated the active curing principle in cinchona which is quinine. The clinical efficacy of quinine has demonstrated itself very well over the last century in the fight against malaria. Information available from the Hospital of Tropical Diseases in London tells us that quinine works by directly attacking the parasite injected into the red blood cells by the malaria-carrying mosquito.

---

[27] Haehl, Richard, ibid.

A more scientific description of the action of quinine is as follows:

"It affects the parasite's intra-erthrocytic mobility and leads to a cessation of haemozoin pigment formation as a result of disturbed or arrested protein metabolism [28]."

Suffice to say that Cullen's astringency theory and Hahnemann's 'like cures like' assumptions were both far off the mark. The amount of cinchona taken by Hahnemann and the symptoms he experienced - redness in cheeks, thirst, shiverings, shakings, quickened pulse, prostration in all the limbs, trembling and an intolerable anxiety, drew this comment from a senior representative of the Department of Infectious Disease and Tropical Medicine in Manchester.

"This amount of quinine in an otherwise healthy adult would not be expected to produce any noticeable symptoms as a single dose. There is no good evidence that quinine affects body temperature one way or the other, unless you actually have malaria, in which case the effects presumably result indirectly from the destruction of the malaria parasites [29]."

Hahnemann's Faulty Experiment

These well qualified observations confirm the waywardness of Hahnemann's original findings and also bear out the objections originally raised by his contemporaries. No one but Hahnemann was able to report these symptoms from cinchona. Were his symptoms the result of auto-suggestion? Did he imagine them? The answer will become emphatically clear later on. What can be said at this point with absolute certainty is that Hahnemann's original faulty experiment *is the cornerstone upon which the empire of homoeopathy rests!*

---

[28] **Taylor, A E R** *Chemotherapeutic Agents and the Study of Parasites*, Blackwell Publication
[29] Personal correspondence

Undeterred by his critics, Hahnemann continued on alone, firmly believing he had been divinely called to lead the new way forward.

> "The only way to heal had not yet been entered upon. It was my lot to proceed along with my own strength and my own means of help. I proceeded, consoled and happy! [30]"

Hahnemann's 'only way to heal' was simply a derivative of the age-old idea of 'like cures like'. A few minutes will now be spent looking at the history of 'like cures like'. Doing so will give a better understanding of the philosophy behind Hahnemann's 'discovery'.

---

[30] Haehl, Richard, ibid.

'Like Cures Like' - A Brief History

Earliest records contain numerous accounts of tribes using animals and birds of various colours in healing rituals. Diseased individuals with, let us say, jaundice or yellow fever would have incantations said over them. The disease would be commanded to leave, and at the same time a yellow bird would be released, flying away with the similarly coloured symptoms and hopefully the disease. In this particular instance, the belief that 'like cures like' (the doctrine of similars), is closely associated with the doctrine of transference - the belief that the disease has transferred from one subject to another. This doctrine has many derivatives.

Abscesses would be wiped with herbs and at the same time, various incantations recited. Then, with sometimes extravagant ritual, these *'newly infected'* herbs would be buried under the footpath leading to the nearest enemy village. The first along the path would then walk over this *'highly charged concoction'* and immediately contract the vile condition (or so it was believed) and then carry it back to infect the rest of his village. In times of warfare, warriors would thrust their spears into the fire in the belief that all wounds inflicted by the spears that day would become searingly painful and inflamed. In countries where belief in voodoo is strong, there is often still a great reluctance to be photographed - the possibility of having one's image stuck with pins or held over a fire a real fear.

Frequent reference is made to Hippocrates, famed for stating:

'Where there is illness there also is the cure.'

Whilst this statement might appear profound, it actually contains very little information that could be considered meaningful. Hippocrates himself never fully clarified this statement. Nevertheless, this quotation is greatly revered in holistic circles and can be found lending credence to the theory of 'like cures like' in a great number of holistic books and magazines.

One of the earliest written records, the Ebers Papyrus (circa 1500 BC), contains many remedies of a quite revolting nature. It was widely believed that the repulsiveness of the 'medication' would forcefully evict the equally revolting disease-causing spirit from the suffering individual. Excrement of ibex and alligator were highly favoured ancient Egyptian cure-alls. The belief that revolting remedies drove out revolting diseases survived for many centuries, and is no more graphically encapsulated than in this delightful little remedy, popularised circa 1660, and used quite widely to 'immunise' oneself against the ravages of the great plague of London:

"Take the brain of a young man that hath died a violent death, together with its membranes, arteries, veins and nerves and all the pith from the backbone. Bruise these in a stone mortar until it becomes a kind of pap, then put in as much spirits of wine as will cover three fingers breadth, digest for half a year in horse dung and take a drop or two in water, once a day [31]."

It was Paracelsus, the 15th century alchemist and physician, who institutionalised another derivative of 'like cures like', or 'the doctrine of signatures'. This is the belief that plants, flowers and leaves of a certain shape are medicinally beneficial for human organs of a similar shape. Hence the names of plants such as heartsease, eyebright, lungwort, spleenwort, liverwort, etc. References to this idea are found in earliest recorded

---

[31] **Camp, John** *The Healer's Art*, F Muller 1978

medical history, but it was Paracelsus who gathered all the strands together to present what he claimed to be his doctrine.

Surviving records also credit Paracelsus with being the first to present the idea of a minute dose to heal according to 'like cures like'. The medieval alchemist was reputed to have cured a town of dysentery by administering to each sufferer a pilule of bread containing a tiny amount of that person's excreta!

Derivatives of 'like cures like' can be found in many of today's leading therapies, not just homoeopathy. This first passage is from Sheila MacNamara's 1995 book, *Traditional Chinese Medicine:*

"Some mental illness is attributed to a heart-spirit problem. Schizophrenia is regarded as a problem of too much heat in the heart, so that the spirit is burnt, making the sufferer restless and violent. The patient would be given medication to calm the heart. Lotus seed sprouts are effective and cooling because the seeds come from the heart of the plant and the lotus grows in water [32]*."*

Julian Scott's 'brain-shaped' walnut remedy for the alleviation of various 'skull inwards' disturbances is similarly dismissed by the professor of plant medicine, Varro Tyler, who writes:

"If [like cures like] *were true, kidney beans should cure all types of renal failure and walnuts should cure various types of cerebral malfunction."*

Professor Tyler goes on to advise his students that an awareness of medical myths such as 'like cures like'

---

[32] **McNamara, Sheila** *Traditional Chinese Medicine*, Hamilton 1995

"...will assist interested persons in distinguishing fact from fiction in a field where the former is scarce and the latter is abundant [33]*."*

It would be interesting to conduct an exit poll at any of the now abundant health stores and find out just how many of the thousands of Bach Flower customers who purchase 'Walnut Remedy' for mental stress, are fully aware of the fanciful myth supporting their £3.00 purchase.

And finally, this comment taken from a lengthy text instructing students on the finer points of flower remedy research is very revealing, making it far easier to understand why these 'researchers' fail so spectacularly to distinguish fact from fiction. It may also serve to encourage the reader to adopt a certain wariness when encountering the term 'flower remedy research'.

"As for making new remedies, there are so many flowers out there, and so many distinct human emotional states. One of the exciting things for me about flower remedies is that there is no objective criterion, no authority, no one who knows the right answer [34]*."*

The opportunities are now endless it seems. To set up a *'remedy'* shop, quite simply, pay no heed to any sensible knowledge base, believe that a complete lack of qualifications is more than made up for by good intention and vivid imagination, proceed to crunch, crush, boil and conjure up anything in the name of medicine and then enjoy a complete freedom to make wild claims as to the efficacy of these concoctions. Buyer beware.

---

[33] **Tyler, Varro** *Herbs of Choice*, Pharmaceutical Products Press 1994
[34] *Cahoots Magazine*. Spring '96 edition

Hahnemann Builds on His Faulty Experiments

Choosing not to dwell on the mythical and wholly inaccurate concept of 'like cures like', writers advocating homoeopathy make much of Hahnemann's experiments. Interestingly, there is nothing in any of their accounts which would make one question the authenticity of his theory.

> *"This experiment was indeed a revelation to Hahnemann as he had actively discovered that a drug which was known to be curative in malaria actually produced the very symptoms of the condition when taken by a healthy person* [35]*"*
>
> *Natural Therapies: A Complete A - Z*

Hahnemann's faulty experiment, today described as an *'active discovery',* led him to the following conclusion. If cinchona gave him the symptoms of fever and it also cured fever, then there were hundreds of substances out there which when taken would produce symptoms similar to the symptoms of hundreds of diseases. It followed surely that all these substances would be the medicines to cure these diseases!

Hahnemann's sole purpose in life had now become quite clear to him. He would need to test all substances in the same way he had tested cinchona. He began to experiment upon himself. He swallowed an incredible variety of substances, including most of the available poisons such as belladonna, lead, strychnine and digitalis. Hahnemann carefully noted all his reactions and symptoms, which in the case of the poisons, were understandably quite violent. It didn't take long for the German pioneer to realise there were too many substances for him to test personally. A certain Dr. Everest, an acquaintance of

---

[35] McCarthy, Margot, ibid.

Hahnemann's, recorded the wayward chemist's next unusual step:

"His own family were pressed into service, and each substance was tried in various doses on many different persons, under every possible variety of circumstances and beneath the immediate inspection of Hahnemann himself [36]."

These experiments began in 1790 and it is not unduly surprising to note that in 1791 Hahnemann's children all became very ill.

" 'Where shall I look for aid?' sighed a disconsolate father on hearing the moaning of his dear, inexpressibly dear sick children. The darkness of night and the dreariness of a desert all around me and no prospect of relief for my oppressed paternal heart [37]".

Seemingly oblivious to the connection, Hahnemann continued to experiment on his family. When it became evident that still more recruits would be required to evaluate the hundreds of crude substances remaining to be tested, he gathered together a number of individuals who became known as his band of *'provers'*. According to Hahnemann, an individual was considered fit to apply for the unenviable post of prover

"... if he is capable of carrying out accurate observations upon himself, if he observes the correct conduct for body and soul, if he is thoroughly imbued and animated by pure and unselfish desire, and if he is willing to sacrifice his time and even jeopardise his health for the acknowledgement of truth [38]."

---

[36] Bradford, Thomas, ibid.
[37] Bradford, Thomas, ibid.
[38] Haehl, Richard, ibid.

The provers would gather at Hahnemann's house to be given a diary and dispensed a particular substance. Taking that substance regularly over the next few days, they would meticulously record all the thoughts, feelings and symptoms they experienced and then return the diaries to Hahnemann. Hahnemann would then pore over this information, collate it and enter it into his ever-growing compendium.

Before looking in more detail at the content of Hahnemann's infamous compendium, it is worth noting that illness dogged Hahnemann's family and colleagues for many years. Franz Hartmann was one of a number of such provers who in later life suffered various chronic conditions. Hartmann's own enthusiasm for Hahnemann's particular methods of research led him to extensively experiment with *nux vomica*, the poison we know as strychnine. He wrote a book based on his findings, and although the connection cannot be fully made, the last years of his life were spent confined to a chair in his bedroom suffering from elephantiasis of the legs, and eventually dying of lung, liver and heart trouble at the age of fifty-seven.

The following observation, made at the time by one of Hahnemann's many critics, although harsh, has a certain prophetic ring to it:

"I fear that a destruction of Hahnemann's whole body and especially of his brain will take place. Really, these kind of experiments should be carried out on criminals deserving a death sentence. If all physicians were to make such experiments upon themselves or wished to make them, I would fear that they might all be crippled in body and soul [39]*."*

---

[39] Haehl, Richard, ibid.

Hahnemann's Ability to Imagine

As one searches through Hahnemann's personal notes on these proving evenings, it becomes clear why no one could reproduce the symptoms Hahnemann susposedly experienced with cinchona. Whilst there is no doubt that Hahnemann would have experienced the most horrendous side-effects and symptoms from some of the substances he swallowed, evidence of Hahnemann's ability to imagine symptoms is starkly captured in this condensed list taken from his book, *Fragmenta de Viribus.*

Substance swallowed	Symptoms reported by Hahnemann	Symptoms reported by colleagues
Acris tinctura	30	0
Arnica Montana	117	33
Capsicum anuum	174	3
Chamomile	272	3
Cocculus	156	6
Drosera	36	4
Ignatia	157	9
Pulsatilla	280	29

It is no longer difficult to understand how Hahnemann was able to record 122 symptoms from his original cinchona experiment when we read that he was also able to record 174 symptoms by eating capsicum (green pepper) and his colleagues just 3! Very plainly he was manufacturing evidence to support his theory. The next time you eat green pepper, record what symptoms if any, you then suffer. Forecast ... none.

In defending these astounding inaccuracies, biographer Richard Haehl declared that *Fragmenta* demonstrated *"extensive observation and a fearless love of truth."* A testament to extensive observation it may be, but a fearless love of truth it most certainly is not! This homoeopathic methodology of proving has not changed to this day, and we will be looking at some eye-opening 20th century examples a little later.

Hahnemann continued meticulously to compile his *Organon of Medicine,* the work that has gone on to become the inspiration and guidance for all modern homoeopathy. In this volume Hahnemann recorded all the known illnesses and their symptoms. He then recorded the hundreds of substances he and his colleagues had swallowed, including all the symptoms they had experienced (and imagined!). He then matched up a substance eliciting symptoms nearest to that of a particular disease. According to Hahnemann, that substance was now *"the assured healing balm".* With all this inaccurate and unorthodox information now in some sort of order, Hahnemann could now at last declare himself ready to prescribe his new healing method to the world.

"Till now nobody has taught this way of healing.... its rays shall irresistibly break through the clouds of prejudice and usher in the dawn of a day which shall shine with a bright and inextinguishable light for the weal of the human race."

Hahnemann's Method of Diagnosis

Hahnemann began his consultations by asking the patient a laborious number of questions, building a clinical picture of the condition based on how the patient looked and felt. If the patient's symptoms were a grey pallor with profuse sweating and through questioning Hahnemann found the patient also suffered from abdominal cramps, he would open his enormous ledger and look up the various symptoms *"grey looking, with sweating ... hmmm. Let's cross reference that with abdominal cramps ... Aha! Strychnine is the cure for this condition, madam."*

Strychnine does indeed produce sweating and severe abdominal cramps and, according to Hahnemann's own interpretation of 'like cures like', would seem the ideal substance to cure this patient's condition.

Original patient records contain details of many noxious substances quite regularly prescribed by Hahnemann according to his theory of 'like cures like'. For stomach pains he prescribed one quarter-ounce doses of mercury. One poor soul was instructed to take half an ounce of sulphuric acid in the morning and another half-ounce the same evening. Once again Hahnemann, his methods and his suffering patients were becoming the focus of much heated debate. Allegations abounded. Against his fellow physicians, Hahnemann levelled charges of butchery and mindless bloodlettings, all the while exhorting his divine calling.

"When I burdened myself with the task of finding help for suffering humanity... I was only carrying out that plan for which The Great Spirit gave me power and insight [40]*."*

---

[40] Haehl, Richard, ibid.

Hahnemann's critics retorted with accusations of charlatanism, quackery and fraud. On his own and ostracised by the medical mainstream, Hahnemann and his doctrine of healing were widely judged to bring little relief and often only further suffering to suffering humanity. To be fair to Hahnemann, his methods were no more injurious than those of his critics. It was Hahnemann's loud and continual trumpeting that his way was the only way which drew such intense criticism. Had he not been quite so vociferous in his claims, Hahnemann may well have been able to continue his particular methods of doctoring almost unnoticed. But the novel practitioner was very much the centre of attention. Quite regularly Dr. Hahnemann's patients would be made worse by a system of healing supposedly revealed to him by God - a bizarre conundrum indeed. A drastic rethink was in order, and with 'similia similibus curentur' facing near total collapse, Hahnemann conceded that his theory, though infallible, might need some refining.

The Birth of 'Less is More'

In refining his theory of 'like cures like', Hahnemann constructed another theory that to this day is arguably the most mystifying theory in the whole of homoeopathic practice. Hahnemann's 'new discovery' was a unique dilution process, which very conveniently decreased the highly poisonous physical properties of his powders, but somehow increased (potentised) their curative powers tremendously. 'Like cures like' had now joined forces with 'less is more'. This was the refinement necessary to perfect what Hahnemann described as his *'rational healing art'*.

The alliance of 'like cures like' and 'less is more' heralded the birth of homoeopathy proper and these two principles remain unchanged to this day. Before examining Hahnemann's 'potentisation' process in more detail together with the whole rationale behind the concept of 'less is more', it is important to note the following: Hahnemann's trial-and-error experiences with cinchona, the dangerous substances which he was continually administering to his family, colleagues and patients, and the general discontent his whole methodology aroused - *these events are rarely reported today in any detail.* One could be forgiven for thinking the history of homoeopathy contained thus far in this book is somehow the wrong script, it bearing so little resemblance to the biographies and potted histories generally available.

The following texts typify the benevolent and inaccurate approach adopted in reporting these chaotic and formative years of homoeopathy:

"In Germany, a brilliant linguist and chemist graduated in medicine in 1799. He found he could bring on the symptoms of a number of fevers by dosing himself with several herbs or herb

extracts. He therefore developed the idea of homoeopathy. His name was Christian Frederick Samuel Hahnemann [41]."

David Bellamy

Richard Haehl writes: *"He suddenly announced without particular explanation very small and so-called infinitesimal doses. Most probably it is to be assumed that the unwelcome aggravations and secondary effects which followed upon remedies being prescribed according to 'the law of similars' induced this keen and careful observer to decrease the doses more and more [42]."*

Magnificent tributes they may be, but they actually shed very little light on the reality of the gruesome poisons so blithely dispensed by our 'keen observer'. Nowhere in any of today's popular books on the subject do we get even a glimpse of the forbidding and positively ugly features fundamental to the true story of homoeopathy. They are the portraits for which Cromwell said he wouldn't pay a farthing! More seriously, these accounts serve also to cement into the psyche of the general populace complete falsities which, with breathtaking casualness, are presented as fact. For instance Richard Haehl quite brazenly tells us that 'like cures like' is actually a law.

Cassels Dictionary defines 'law' as:

"The orderly recurrence of natural phenomena, an invariable sequence of events."

The Oxford English Dictionary gives a similar definition of the word 'law':

---

[41] **Bellamy, David** *Blooming Bellamy*, BBC Books 1993
[42] Haehl, Richard, ibid.

40

"A factual statement of what always happens in certain circumstances."

On the balance of the abundant evidence, Hahnemann's experiments, which gave birth to his famous 'law' 'similia similibus curentur', **are totally devoid of orderliness, certainty, accuracy, repeatability or fact,** and cannot in any way fall under the correct definition of the word 'law'. To compound these gross inaccuracies still further, when even the briefest study is made of homoeopathy, it is found that 'similia similibus' is simply a derivative of the much wider philosophical concept of 'like cures like', a centuries old falsity, most definitely not a foundation upon which to build and develop sensible medicine. Homoeopathy's 'similia similibus curentur' is no more than attractive, intuitively compelling folklore.... not law!

Our appreciation of the extent to which total error can be made to sound feasible assists us in shedding new light on pseudo-scientific statements such as this one, taken from *Homoeopathy - Medicine For the 21st Century:*

"The law of similars is not simply a philosophical construct but is a practical guide to prescribing a medicine that will heal [43]*"*

Referring to homoeopathy as *'a medicine that will heal'* reminds us that despite its untenable foundations, homoeopathy must hold some sort of curing mechanism somewhere. It is by taking a closer look at Hahnemann's special potentisation process that we can discover the reasons for homoeopathy's much publicised success. And once again we will find that we have not been given the full story by any means.

---

[43] **Ullmann, Dana** *Homoeopathy - Medicine for the 21st Century,* Thorsons 1989

Potentisation - A Closer Look

The streaming eyes and running nose one suffers when chopping onions makes this vegetable an ideal candidate for a 'like cures like' remedy for the common cold. And indeed, in homoeopathy today, the onion is a very popular remedy for this condition. But for this onion to become a homoeopathic remedy it must first undergo 'potentisation'. Hahnemann explains:

"In a special process unknown before my time, homoeopathy develops the inner spirit-like medicinal powers of crude substances, to a degree hitherto unheard of, and makes all of them exceedingly, even immeasurably penetratingly effective, even those that in their crude state do not have the slightest medicinal effect on the human organism [44]*."*

Let's now look at this potentisation process which, according to Hahnemann, develops the onion's *"inner spirit-like medicinal powers to a degree hitherto unheard of."*

The homoeopath first prepares the basic formula. The onion is chopped up and mixed with an equal amount of distilled water and left to stand in a stoppered jar for approximately one month. This results in 'the mother tincture'. One drop of the mother tincture is then added to a test-tube containing ninety-nine drops of distilled water. The test-tube is shaken vigorously for about one minute and then rapped sharply against a hard surface, Hahnemann insisting this hard surface to be a leather-bound book. The contents of the test-tube are now considered to be potentised to the power of 1c. According to Julian Scott, author of *Natural Remedies for Women*, this shaking and rapping process *"...spreads the remedy's energy and vibrations through the preparation* [45]*."*

---

[44] Hahnemann, Christian Samuel, ibid.
[45] **Scott, Julian** *Natural Remedies for Women*, Gaia 1991

One drop of this 'potentised' solution is then added to a second test-tube containing ninety-nine drops of distilled water. The same shaking and rapping process takes place, potentising the solution another centesimal to the power of 2c. At this early stage of dilution, the original onion extract is already barely traceable in the solution, but the onion's *'healing vibrations'* are apparently becoming manifoldly increased with each shake. The process continues ad infinitum, a test-tube marked 30c denoting the shaking, rapping and diluting process has taken place thirty times.

Trevor Smith tells us in *Talking about Homoeopathy,*

"The 6c potency is one which is commonly used for first aid and local problems and one which is valuable for home use [46]*."*

6c remedies now account for the vast majority of over-the-counter homoeopathic sales in High Street chemists and health shops in the UK. It is interesting to note at this stage just how little of the original substance actually remains in a 6c remedy. The mathematical formula to work out the number of times a substance may be divided before it is rendered non-existent was first formulated by Avogadro, the 19th century Italian chemist, in his treatise on the divisibility of gases.

To determine the amount of onion present in a 6c remedy of Allium Cepa, budding chemists might have no problem applying Avogadro's formula of 6.02×10. For the less scientifically minded, the following example serves as a reasonably accurate measure. Fill Wembley Stadium to the roof with water. To this vast amount of water add one single drop of onion mother tincture. Stir thoroughly. Fill your test-tube with this Wembley mixture. Your test-tube now contains a measure of onion

---

[46] **Smith, Trevor** *Talking About Homoeopathy,* Insight 1986

equivalent to 6c [47]. 12c is equivalent to one drop of mother tincture added to the Atlantic Ocean. Literally nothing remains! The inescapable reality that homoeopathic remedies are so weak highlights the great divide between the theory of *'less is more'* and plain common sense. Referring to Avogadro's formula, homoeopathic author Dana Ullmann acknowledges that although their solutions may not contain anything of the original substance in them,

"... something remains, the essence of the substance, its resonance, its energy, its pattern [48]*."*

So how do homoeopathic tablets with literally nothing in them appear to work so effectively? There are very straightforward explanations for this seeming mystery and these will be discussed shortly. But first, let's briefly look at a selection of writings highlighting the nonsensical concept of 'less is more'.

In yet another of his wholly fraudulent episodes, Hahnemann claimed he had discovered the cure for typhoid. One sceptical enquirer asked Hahnemann whether putting a cupful of the appropriate remedy in Lake Geneva would provide a cure for the whole of Europe. Hahnemann replied, *"If I could shake the lake, then I would do exactly this* [49]*."*

Comments such as these did little to enhance Hahnemann's reputation, and his theory of 'less is more' fuelled the wit of many a critic. The following wry anecdote is found in the memoirs of Heine, a poet and writer of the time:

[47] **Bambridge, A D** *Homoeopathy - Results Beyond Reason* 1992
[48] Ullmann, Dana, ibid.
[49] Bambridge, A D, ibid.

Whilst on a train journey, Heine met the violinist Ernst who gave him a large Lyons sausage to give to his homoeopathic doctor in Paris. Heine and his wife had prepared no food for their long train journey and between them they ate most of the sausage. On reaching Paris, Heine cut off a minute amount from the remaining sliver of sausage, and posted it to the homoeopath with these words:

"Mein Herr, your research maintains that a millionth part can have the greatest possible effect. Please receive a millionth part of a Lyons sausage which Herr Ernst asked me to give you. If there is any truth in homoeopathy, it will have the same effect on you as if had sent you the whole sausage [50]."

Concerning Hahnemann's mysterious shaking and rapping process, a Dr Mombert at the time was much less good humoured:

"An idea which yields nothing to the wildest freaks of the madhouse. The thought of this nonsense makes one giddy. In fact giddiness plays a very great part in the whole theory of homoeopathy. The idea is worthy of being recorded in the annals of the most notorious lunatic asylum [51]."

Mombert goes on to ask how a man of such obvious intelligence

"... can trumpet forth a theory so thoroughly false?"

Common sense tells us that continued dilution can only decrease the strength of that which is being diluted. The following texts taken from modern-day homoeopathic literature

---

[50] **Glasscheib, Dr H S** *The March of Medicine*, McDonald & Co 1963
[51] Haehl, Richard, ibid.

and comment attempt to explain why we should ditch common sense and blindly believe that 'less is more':

"For any given plane in space, the presence of a sphere evokes a point; for any given point a plane. I cannot stop to explain the comparatively simple construction by means which this happens. The mutual relation is literally one of expansion and contraction."

George Adams - *Potentisation and Peripheral Forces of Nature*

...who further states:

"To the laws of parallelism must be added those of the right angle and of angular measure generally. These too are determined from the infinite periphery inward. The way in which this happens would take too long to explain in the present context [52]."

Readers wishing to fathom any of the above should take comfort from the fact that as yet not one single homoeopathic pharmacist has been able to coherently explain Mr Adams' reasoning. A senior pharmacist at Weleda, the homoeopathic manufacturing company which sent me George Adams' essay, stated *"I'm afraid I can't help you in this instance, I was never that good at geometry anyway."*

"Here, again we begin to approach the deeper aspects of philosophy and I do not intend to say any more about it here. The method of preparing the remedies and how they act is not essential to the understanding of homoeopathy [53]."

Chris Hammond - *How To Use Homoeopathy*

---

[52] **Adams, George** *in a lecture given to British Congress of Homoeopaths, June 1961*
[53] **Hammond, Chris** *How To Use Homoeopathy*, Element Books 1991

"Look, there are some things which you just have to accept."
Quality Control, Nelson & Co

"By grinding and succussing (potentisation) more energy is built up in the molecules in rather the same way as people who are crammed into a railway compartment have more 'burst-out' energy when the train stops than a similar number of people sitting in a row of seats."
Dr. Andrew Stanway - *Alternative Medicine*

The above texts typify the great number of explanations in circulation, none of which bring any clarity to the glibly quoted phrase 'less is more'. And whilst it is quite true that there are some things which we just have to accept, 'less is more' need not be one of them. It is a nonsensical concept which we can quite rightly reject. Less is less. It always has been and always will be!

"In the holy act of potentisation, healing energy is released from the shackles of earthly structure to regenerate harmony in the ailing organism [54]."
J Angerer - Homoeopath

This last text is one of many which quite openly detail the more 'hubble-bubble' type approach to the subject of potentisation. In his *The Natural Health Handbook*, Anthony Campbell highlights the divisions existing between homoeopaths who believe the remedies contain unearthly powers and those who insist there is a scientific basis for homoeopathy's mode of action.

"Hahnemann took the concept of the vital force and made it the cornerstone of his theory... Hahnemann often speaks of

---

[54] **Pfeiffer, Dr Samuel** *Healing At Any Price*, Word Publications 1988

dynamisation as releasing spiritual forces in the medicines. Some of his successors found these references to the vital force, dynamisation and spiritual forces dangerous and undesirable, since they made homoeopathy into a kind of metaphysical system. To a considerable extent the subsequent development of homoeopathy is the story of the interplay and rivalry that occurred between these two schools [55]*."*

Today there are many homoeopaths who try to explain 'less is more' and 'potentisation' in purely scientific terms. The following texts demonstrate the homeopath's brilliant ability to identify scientific data with homoeopathic foundations, reasoning which at first glance appears convincing, but upon examination is found to be completely irrational.

"For example, the salmon can detect the scent of their home water in a dilution of one part in 1,000,000 and the human nose is capable of detecting mercaptan at concentrations of only one part in 500,000,000,000 parts of air [56]*."*
Andrew Lockie - *The Family Guide to Homoeopathy*

I contacted Mr. Lockie in order to establish his sources for the above information, and to ask him whether he thought these examples were really that relevant to the debate. Mr. Lockie was not able to give me the source for either of his examples and conceded that perhaps his line of reasoning was not relevant to the argument for the smaller dose.

Brian Inglis defends the efficacy of the minute dose in a similarly inaccurate but equally convincing manner:

"Perhaps the most striking confirmation of homoeopathic theory has come out of recent investigations into LSD.

---

[55] **Campbell, Anthony** *Natural Health Handbook*, QED Books 1991
[56] **Lockie, Dr Andrew** *Family Guide to Homoeopathy*, Hamish Hamilton 1990

Dr. Albert Hoffman, who developed it in Switzerland, found that a dose too small to be seen by the naked eye, a quantity weighing 1/200,000 of an ounce, was enough to create reactions in the human mind [57]."

To suggest that a minute amount of pure, undiluted and exceptionally potent LSD is in any way comparable to a highly diluted and even non-existent homoeopathic dose is grossly misleading and once again demonstrates the extent to which intellect must be jettisoned in order to defend 'less is more'.

Frequent reference is made to quantum physics, 'vibratory patterns, resonance, energy imprints', etc. However, when it comes to furnishing the reader with direct evidence that diluting a substance increases potency and strength, we are always told the proof lies in tomorrow.

*"The possibility that water has a memory is now being raised, that in some way it retains in its structure some trace of things it has previously been in contact with. There is now some fairly high-powered physics that says that this indeed **may be a reality** [58]."*

Peter Fisher - *Homoeopathy - A Realistic Alternative*

The scientific fact most frequently distorted in order to support the homoeopathic theories of 'like cures like' and 'less is more' is that of immunisation. The introduction into the body system of a minute amount of dead virus to prevent the same disease does indeed sound similar to the homoeopathic principle of 'like cures like'. This text from *Homoeopathy - Medicine for the 21st Century* is a typical example:

---

[57] **Inglis, Brian** *Fringe Medicine*, Faber & Faber 1964

[58] **Homoeopathy: A Realistic Alternative,** a video commentary by Materia Medica Comms. 1993

"Immunisation is based on the principle of similars. No lesser person than Dr Emil Adolph Von Behring, the 'father of immunology', directly pointed to the origins of immunology when he asserted:

"By what technical term could we more appropriately speak of this influence than by Hahnemann's homoeopathy?"

Modern allergy treatment likewise utilises the homoeopathic approach by the use of small doses of allergens in order to create an antibody response [59]."

To the lay reader this may well sound impressive. However, Dr. Samuel Pfeiffer, author of *Healing At Any Price,* reveals the very high degree of error that abounds in such comparisons:

"A favourite argument to support homoeopathic theories is the analogy with immunisation. Isn't this an accepted method - to heal like with like? Subcutaneous injections of dead or weakened viruses are able to prevent exactly those diseases which are caused by the viruses.

Although this is true in some cases, homoeopaths do not say that this preventative measure only applies to a very few of the more than 10,000 known diseases. Neither do they attempt to demonstrate that homoeopathic remedies activate the same immune mechanisms that are stimulated by a vaccination. It would be futile to try to compare the two, as these mechanisms do not apply to homoeopathy. These examples show however how scientific discoveries are taken out of context to support bizarre claims [60]."

The last word on the potentisation process is left to the founder of homoeopathy, Samuel Hahnemann.

"By shaking, the latent medicinal power is wonderfully

---

[59] Ullman, Dana, ibid.
[60] Pfeiffer, Dr Samuel, ibid.

liberated and vitalised.... a spiritualising of the inner medicinal powers by removing the covering of natural forces. This spirit-like force by itself is no longer perceptible to the senses... [61] *"*

What realms are we entering now?

[61] Hahnemann, Christian Samuel, ibid.

Homoeopathy's Occult Foundations

Hahnemann was convinced his special potentisation process was uncovering and unleashing an incredibly powerful spiritual essence which he believed lay dormant in all matter. His *Organon of Medicine* states

"...potentisation unlocks the natural substances. It uncovers and reveals the specific medicinal powers lying hidden in their soul [62]*."*

For almost twenty years, the influential Mason and alchemist Johann Starck had been travelling Europe instructing the brethren of the Lodge on separating man's spiritual essence from his terrestrial nature. Inspired by the same philosophy, Hahnemann was simply giving similar instruction on separating the spiritual essence of animal, vegetable and mineral.

Of course, these ideas were not new - there is nothing new under the sun. Hahnemann was on that well-trodden path supposedly leading to the discovery of the invisible fifth essence which, according to the alchemist, permeates all matter and holds the whole universe together. Discovering this essence, separating it from matter and bottling it was the alchemist's ultimate goal, above even that of turning base metal into gold. Whoever could isolate the vital force, the fifth essence (the 'quintessence' as Paracelsus called it), would be in possession of 'the elixir of life', bringing untold riches to its discoverer and vibrant health and immortality to all!

The belief that all matter contains some invisible force has been with us for a very long time. Since written records began, men have been 'down in the lab', mixing, scraping, boiling and refining in their quest for the elixir of life.

---

[62] Hahnemann, Christian Samuel, ibid.

Hahnemann was accused of building on the ideas of Paracelsus. This passage is from one of Paracelsus' many alchemic works which were widely read in Hahnemann's era, and no doubt would have graced the shelves of Herr Brukenthal's immense library.

"Doctors, I advise you to use alchemy in preparing magnalia, mysteria and arcana, and to separate the pure from the impure so that you may obtain a perfect medicine. God did not choose to give us the medicines prepared. He wants us to cook them ourselves [63]."

The difficulties faced by present-day homoeopaths to coherently explain homoeopathy's potentisation process are not at all surprising. In fact there never will be a coherent explanation for Hahnemann's shaking and rapping which *"liberates and vitalises latent powers"* because quite evidently the central tenets of homoeopathy are rooted in the occult practice of alchemy. Is it any wonder that Chris Hammond wishes not to explore further *"the deeper aspects of this philosophy"*?

Hahnemann's diaries of this period contain a great deal of astrological and alchemic symbolism. He would often work long into the night, mixing, scraping, cooking and stirring his concoctions. Very soon Hahnemann possessed a vast array of 'potentised' liquids and it was with these remedies that his patients suddenly began to get better. Hahnemann was becoming known as the doctor whose patients actually recovered! He was not interested in the arguments rejecting his mystical remedies - so far as he was concerned, his patients' recoveries proved the worth of homoeopathy.

---

[63] **Pachter, H** *Paracelsus*, Henry Schuman 1951

It is no different today. Homoeopathic author Andrew Lockie tells us that

"... many homoeopaths are not interested in providing proof, because they know from their own experience that it works [64]."

Homoeopaths acknowledge that nothing physical remains in the remedies. Hahnemann believed his remedies contained invisible spirit energy, the fifth essence, the vital force. And again it is no different today. The alchemic/vitalist philosophy remains unchanged. In his book *What is Homoeopathy?* Dr Nelson Brunton gives us this description of the supposed invisible energy in the remedies:

*"According to homoeopathy, the **vital force** activates the body and promotes healing. This energy permeates all of nature, and without it, nothing can exist [65]."*

In order for homoeopathy to make any sense at all, one must first adopt the basic philosophy underpinning the therapy, the philosophy of the vital force. To those who have recovered from illness and attributed their recovery to homoeopathy, it can only be because the 'medicine' is pulsating with Hahnemann's mystical vital force energy!

For those uneasy with this idea - help is at hand. Let's now look at the factors which clearly explain why Hahnemann's patients suddenly began to get better and why these homoeopathic remedies containing nothing appear to work so effectively today.

---

[64] Lockie, Dr Andrew, ibid.
[65] **Brunton, Dr Nelson** *Homoeopathy*, Optima 1989

The Truth Behind Homoeopathy's Success

In the many books on homoeopathy, frequent reference is made to our susceptibility to illness, but rarely is anything written that gives us insight into just how wonderfully equipped the human body is to overcome the majority of these illnesses completely unaided.

Self-Limiting Illness

Fifty years ago, very little was known about our immune system. It was known that there were cells in the blood that helped to defend the body against disease, but what these cells did and how they did it was a mystery. Today immunology is a whole science and knowledge of the body's defence systems is growing all the time. Along with the red cells carrying oxygen, and big white cells that fight any foreign germs they can find, the blood stream carries millions of little round white cells called lymphocytes. T lymphocytes which originate in the thymus gland and B lymphocytes from the bone marrow are just two of the highly organised battalions of germ killers that make up the army defending us from infectious attack.

Dr Paul Brand has written extensively on the unique design of the human body and he explores some of the amazing aspects of this in-built army in his book, *The Forever Feast*. In the following passage Dr Brand focuses our attention on a subject which homoeopathy never discusses.

"I must share just one facet of the skills of the T lymphocytes, because I get excited at the ingenuity that must have gone into their design, and because I'm so happy to have these little guys on my side when I am sick. My T lymphocytes concentrate in

places where most germs try to get into the body. It is never very long before an invading germ meets a T lymphocyte.

The first wonderful thing is that the lymphocyte knows at once that this living cell is not 'one of us', it is an enemy. The next wonderful thing is what it does. It inspects the enemy cell and takes a template or pattern of its surface, noting especially the weak points. Then our friend runs back to the factory where new cells are made and announces the emergency: "An enemy has entered the body and is rapidly multiplying. We have to manufacture antibodies of exactly this shape, so that the enemy will be killed and no other cell will be harmed."

An older lymphocyte may hurry up at this point and tell the factory that the shape of the needed antibodies is exactly the size as was used a year ago, when there was a brief war in the body during the flu season. Therefore there is no need to repeat the time-consuming preparation of the prototype antibodies - we already have them. All that is needed is to rush into mass production. Thus before the virus has time to do any real harm, masses of specific antibodies are all over the body, overcoming every last virus, and restoring health and wholeness everywhere [66]."

Concerning the amazing nature of our body's natural defence system, Dr. John Dwyer, clinical immunologist and author of *Body at War*, writes:

"The capacity of lymphocytes to recognise, 'learn' by experience, retain memory function and have the self-discipline to act differently, yet appropriately in varying situations makes such cells truly wondrous creations of nature.

---

[66] **Brand, Dr Paul** *The Forever Feast*, Monarch Publications 1994

When nine-year-old Christine fell from her bike onto a thorny bush, she sustained minor abrasions to her hands and major bruises to her ego as her accident had resulted from her inability to keep up with her eleven-year-old brother. Her mother washed her hands, placed a kiss and a Band Aid over the small cut on the hand and life went on. Into that minor wound however had entered some bacteria picked up from the thorns and the next day they were making their presence felt.

In various strategic sites in our body, immune stations have been established called lymph nodes. Vessels in the skin (those that run beside blood vessels) have fluid circulating in them called lymph. Lymph vessels and lymph itself supply a highway and a transport medium for T cells, and can pick up the invading antigen that has pierced the skin and transport it via the strong current of lymph flow to the nearest lymph node.

Once Christine's invaders reached her lymph nodes she recovered quickly, for numerous cells were dispatched to kill the organisms present in her lymph vessels, and anywhere else for that matter [67]."

And a final word on the body's defence systems from Lennart Nilsson, author of *The Body Victorious*:

"Suddenly the sight of injury, previously so peaceful is transformed into a battlefield on which the body's armed forces hurl themselves repeatedly at the encroaching micro-organisms, crushing and annihilating them. No one is pardoned, no prisoners are taken....

All these events take place in a microscopic world where nothing, neither the body's cells nor the micro-organisms that

---

[67] **Dwyer, Dr John** *Body at War*, Unwin Hyman 1988

assail them, measures more than a few thousandths of a millimetre across [68] *."*

Using Dr. Dwyer's account of Christine's cycling injury, let us compare the conventional approach with the homoeopathic approach to the treatment of a simple cut. In Dr. Dwyer's example, Mum did all the right things. She checked her daughter's cut was not too serious. She washed it thoroughly, applied a plaster to it, and gave her daughter a kiss. Christine's in-built germ-fighting army saw to the practical side of things and Mum's loving ministrations brought a smile back to her little girl's face. Needless to say, Christine made a quick and complete recovery.

According to homoeopathic thinking however, the sophisticated mechanisms governing Christine's healing process are not as intelligent or all-knowing and self-sufficient as Drs Brand, Dwyer and Nilsson would have us believe. Homoeopathy teaches that the body's natural healing mechanisms are stimulated into action by the administration of the appropriate homoeopathic remedy. The Homoeopathic Foundation tells us:

"Homoeopathic remedies assist the patient to regain health by stimulating the body's natural forces [69] *."*

A homoeopath prescribes a remedy, convinced that s/he is assisting in 'kick-starting' the body's intricate healing mechanisms into action. For a cut such as Christine's, homoeopath Miranda Castro advises the following remedies:

aconite - more commonly known as wolves bane, so called because hunters would dip their arrows in this very poisonous

---

[68] **Nilsson, Lennart** *Body Victorious*, Faber 1987
[69] Homoeopathic Development Foundation Information leaflet

substance before setting out on a wolf hunt. **belladonna** - deadly nightshade. **lachesis** - snake venom. **phosphoric acid** - a poisonous rust proofing agent which Ms Castro especially recommends when blood is slow to clot! Not only do homoeopaths falsely and quite dangerously promote the idea that these remedies enhance the coagulation process, they also tell us that further remedies are required to assist in the healing of the cut itself.

According to homoeopathic thinking there is a choice of remedy depending on what part of the body has been cut. Had Christine cut her shin, ruta would be the ideal remedy, ruta being an evergreen shrub, used centuries ago for coughs and colds and as a powerful influence to ward off witches. Because it was her hand that was cut, Ms Castro's recommendation is ledum, another evergreen shrub, native to northern Europe and used by the Scandinavians to rid their cattle of lice. Homoeopath Chris Hammond recommends hypericum, more commonly known as St John's Wort. For centuries St John's Wort had been associated with healing wounds, due to the holes in its leaves resembling the pores of the skin and the reddish juice, which can be expressed from the flower resembling blood - a remedy from Paracelsus' doctrine of signatures.

Not one of the above substances (phosphoric acid, shrubbery, etc.) plays any part in the intricate process leading to the coagulation of blood or the healing of a cut. These wildly inaccurate ideas are the direct result of Miranda Castro, Chris Hammond et al, consulting and building on Hahnemann's nonsensical *Organon of Medicine*. Hahnemann's deluded thinking led him to believe that he could create incredibly powerful medicines out of substances

"... that even in their crude state do not have the slightest medical effect on the human body."

Miranda Castro explains the history behind some of the 'powerful medicines' known only to homoeopathy:

"Salt, by and large, was thought to have little medicinal value until Hahnemann conducted his provings in 1820. An uncommon symptom that will lead you to prescribe Natruni Muriaticum (salt) is that these people are completely unable to pass urine in the presence of others.

Sand - is almost unknown as a medicine outside homoeopathy. Silica (sand) [useful for individuals who sweat at night.] *The sweat smells sour and their feet are characteristically sweaty and smelly, to the point of eating holes in their socks.*

The raw ink from the cuttlefish is not fit for medicinal use and indeed was unknown as a medicine until Hahnemann observed that a sickly artist friend of his licked his paintbrush frequently as he worked. He made a potency of the Sepia ink and cured the artist of his complaints [70]*."*

And so it continues. Salt, sand, squid ink, etc., with no medicinal value whatsoever, is shaken, stirred and diluted to the point where it no longer exists - and then bottled. These empty remedies now lining the 'natural health' shelves by the thousands are very deceptively assuming grand medicinal status, disguised as Natrum Muriaticum, Silica, Sepia, and so on.

There can be no doubt that Latin terminology on the labels plays a vital role in perpetuating the myth that homoeopathy is

---

[70] **Castro, Miranda** *Complete Homoeopathy*, MacMillan Press 1990

somehow a respectable form of medicine. It is easy to see how the anglicising of homoeopathy's some two thousand, mostly non-medicinal substances would be quite disastrous in terms of customer appeal and subsequent sales. Who would seriously consider buying nitric acid, mercury, plaster of paris, gunpowder, conkers, squid ink and strychnine as medicine?

Mercifully, these substances suggested for Christine's cut by Ms Castro, Chris Hammond et al have been diluted beyond existence anyway, and would cause no harm if taken. In fact the harmlessness of the homoeopathic remedies in themselves is well known. Hospitals and poison centres often receive calls from needlessly, but quite understandably anxious parents who have found their child clutching an empty bottle of homoeopathic pills. At a deeper level however, a certain harm is being wrought here. That most damaging ingredient, the yeast of false belief, has worked its way quite insidiously into the batch, causing some fundamental misunderstandings to arise. Having some sort of handle on the truth behind homoeopathy, the fog which has settled over us like a thick blanket, would very quickly evaporate. Crooked thinking would be straightened and there would be no more calls to casualty over expensive little pills containing nothing - Mum and Dad wouldn't even have them in the house!

With tongue in cheek, this whole scenario could be summed up quite nicely by stealing one of Hahnemann's earlier quotes and adapting it only slightly *"Till now, few have grasped these homoeopathic fallacies so.... but soon the truth about homoeopathy shall irresistibly break through the clouds of prejudice, shining with a bright and inextinguishable light for the weal of the human race."* ...the weal in this instance being the weal of irrational belief, the consequences of which we shall touch upon later.

In amongst all this bizarre homoeopathic advice it is not surprising that no mention is made of the fact that patients such as Christine would have made a full recovery anyway! Cuts and bruises are just two of the many aches, pains and ailments very efficiently combated by our wonderful immune system. Coughs, colds, flu, headaches, dizziness, temperatures, strains and sprains, stomach upsets, sickness and minor viral infections, are all illnesses that in the main are conquered without the need for medical intervention[71]. These illnesses are known as 'self-limiting' and it is no coincidence that homoeopathic remedies containing nothing show excellent results in all of these conditions.

Had Christine been given homoeopathic tablets for her cut, she would definitely have enjoyed taking them as Nelson Brunton notes in his book *Homoeopathy* :

"Since most of the tablets are sugar-based, they are not unpleasant to take. Children in particular seem to look forward to this type of medicine [72]*."*

To the uninformed observer, the combination of taking a homoeopathic remedy and recovering soon afterwards (an all too common phenomenon in homoeopathy), confers upon these medicinally inert tablets considerable healing properties.

The *Mail on Sunday* recently ran a pullout section entitled *Ultimate Health*. In part one, Michele B. was asked to try out homoeopathy over a period of a few weeks at the Wimbledon Clinic of Natural Medicine.

Week 1. "He prescribed some homoeopathic drops for my cough and intestinal bug, slow-release vitamin C and

---

[71] If symptoms persist, advice should always be sought from a qualified GP.
[72] Brunton, Dr Nelson, ibid.

bioflavanoids to clear up the remains of infection and some helpful capsules, called ME1, to work on the immune system, circulation and energy production. He explained these are quite general remedies until he sees how my body reacts. The thought of finding out what is going on in my body is encouraging and I feel quite optimistic." **£60**

Week 2. "No particular change. I still feel positive but I'm not sure I feel better, except I do have slightly more energy in the evenings. The stomach bug still has not disappeared, but I know homoeopathic remedies don't work overnight and I certainly don't feel worse." **£35**

Week 3. "Amazing! I do feel better, definitely [73]" **£35**

The onion and its use as a remedy for the common cold is a classic example of the mythology surrounding homoeopathy's success. There is actually no cure for the common cold. It runs its natural course and after about three days our immune system has gained the victory. However it is not uncommon for a homoeopath to recommend potentised onion, saying: *"Within three days of taking this, my cold disappeared completely!"*

The 1st century writer and semi-physician Pliny has some wonderful remedies lovingly recorded in his book *Encyclopedia of the Natural World*. For a headache Pliny recommends the genitals of a male fox to be tied around the forehead. 20th century homoeopathy lists over fifty types of headache and as many different remedies to cure them. Substances considered efficacious for a headache and then diluted beyond existence include oyster shell, coffee, arsenic, squid ink, flintstone, rhododendron, and nitric acid.

---

[73] *Ultimate Health Magazine,* Mail on Sunday, Feb 1996

For corns, Pliny recommends we lay on our backs under the night sky, within hearing distance of a squeaky door hinge, whilst looking out for a shooting star. Pliny assures us that spotting one will cause the corn to fall off within the month. For the same condition Miranda Castro recommends club moss and flintstone again diluted beyond existence and taken at regular intervals. One is tempted to ask whose remedies are the more advanced!

Exactly the same question could be asked of any number of 'hands on' therapies out there today. The lucrative crystal market with their mysterious *vibrational frequencies* and *sympathetic resonance*, is just one example, all this *vibrational* thinking of course being only a hop and a skip away from Hahnemann's own pulsating *life force* philosophy. For an equivalent *'Pliny/crystal'* experience, simply lay on your back, let the crystal therapist tell you all about the huge benefits to be had from placing various brightly coloured gems on *strategically important points* on your body, and then, at the end of the ceremony, within hearing distance of the till registering £30 upwards for this imaginative half hour service, believe the said complaint has gone!

In his book, *Let's Talk About Homoeopathy,* Trevor Smith discusses *"noises that make you sick"* and describes how he treats this condition.

"Low frequency pollution or 'hum' is now recognised as a major health hazard for many. A woman of 60 came with a problem of generalised headaches and insomnia, since being exposed in her home to low frequency noise from a large industrial cold store about a quarter of a mile away. A homoeopathic pharmacist made a potency of low frequency noise by exposing a fifty per cent ethanol water mix to the

vibrations in the area for forty-eight hours. It was then made up to 6c. The results were rapid and startling. The patient phoned after a fortnight to say how much better she felt [74]*."*

Whilst flintstone, nitric acid, rhododendron and 'potentised noise' must surely prompt concern over homoeopathy's widespread misuse of the term 'medicine', these remedies pale into insignificance alongside the more mystical chemistry currently taking place in the UK's leading homoeopathic laboratories. Both Starck and Paracelsus would be most interested to learn that Luna and Sol Britannic have now been transmuted into medicines. Otherwise known as moonlight and sunlight, these two 'extracts' are available in potentised tablet form from the Helios Pharmacy, Tunbridge Wells, Kent.

Homoeopaths Bob Lawrence and Lesley King explain their preparation of potentised moonlight:

"The Luna was prepared from the emanations of the full harvest moon on 7th October 1987. Ethyl alcohol solution was exposed directly to the moon's rays with a mirror positioned behind the vial to reflect the emanations back through the solution to intensify the irradiation process. Another solution of milk sugar was exposed in a crystal bowl with the sugar stirred periodically.... This mixture was potentised up to 30c and beyond [75]*."*

The full story of potentised moonlight is found in King and Lawrence's handbook, *Luna - A Proving*. It is apparent from their writings that the mixing, shaking, stirring and rapping process has not changed since Hahnemann's day and neither has the methodology of proving:

---

[74] Smith, Trevor, ibid.
[75] **Lawrence & King** *Luna - A Proving*, Helios Pharmacy 1993

"The lunar proving was carried out along the lines laid out by Hahnemann. Each prover was issued with a diary in which they were to record any mental, emotional and physical changes [76]."

The following is a condensed list of symptoms recorded by one prover taking potentised moonlight over a period of approximately fourteen days.

"I took the remedy last thing at night. The first day I awoke after having had a vivid dream. I developed a mouth ulcer. As the day passed my lips began to get very dry and my thirst more compelling. I ached all over and a tingling in my breast drove me frantic. By day seven I was quite disoriented. Food felt strange and offensive in my mouth. I made many mistakes in speaking and confusing tenses. It was as if I was no longer connected up as an integrated human being.

Day eight: Found it hard to live according to the clock, structures are melting away.

Day nine: I feel a silence between me and the outside world.

Day fourteen: Irritated by my children [77]."

Homoeopath Jeremy Sherr has conducted many similar studies on the supposed effects of different substances. The following symptoms were recorded by provers taking crushed scorpion at a potency of 6c.

"Pushed children out of bed with no compassion. Did shopping in a very disorganised manner. A friend commented

---

[76] Lawrence & King, ibid.
[77] Lawrence & King, ibid.

I did not look like myself. Felt I was driving slowly - could not judge the speed of cars."

"A desire to break things. Just a black thunder within me, eyes staring full of hate, just looking at the children sends them frantic."

"In the evening became manic, stalked the streets, believed my umbrella was a knife."

"In a public place, jumped up and played antics, though many people watched, did not care."

"Dreamed I was being chased by my husband. Awoke terrified and hit him in the eye [78]*."* And probably in a lovely, deep sleep, poor chap!

Mr. Sherr's homoeopathic writings on the effects of chocolate contain reports of the following symptoms:

'a desire to cut my hair short'
'a fear of cockroaches'
'a heaviness at the base of the brain'
'I get lesions and the room starts flickering [79]*'*

Allow this to sink in all these bizarre events are taking place today under the umbrella of research. Individuals are actually convincing themselves that one or two drops of potentised moonlight are causing their life structures to melt away, and that chocolate brings on a craving for a haircut! Astronomer Patrick Moore's April Fool wheeze brought forth similarly outrageous stories. On reporting that the convergence of various planetary paths might cause some parts of the globe to experience weightlessness, the Sky at Night switchboard was inundated with callers who felt strangely lighter on their feet, with some people reporting their heads even brushing the ceiling.

---

[78] **Sherr, Jeremy** *Homoeopathic Proving of Scorpion*, Helios 1990
[79] **Sherr, Jeremy** *Homoeopathic Proving of Chocolate*, Helios 1993

All these wild and totally subjective homoeopathic imaginings are collected up just as in Hahnemann's day and put into meticulous order. *'Feel like breaking things', 'thought umbrella was a knife', 'in the evening became manic'* and *'a fear of cockroaches'* are entered into the homoeopathic repertory thus:-

Anger, in the evening ....under A
Break things, desire to ....under B
Cockroaches, fear of ....under C
Delusion, thought umbrella was knife ....under D

The information is then ready to be transferred to CD-Rom/floppy disc, finishing up a most professional looking package. Unfortunately it is not apparent from the numerous homoeopathic programmes now available, that the actual software contains so much unorthodox, illogical and totally bizarre information, of no clinical value whatsoever.

The Power of Placebo

Mary, who is consulting a homoeopath for the first time and discussing her heavy cold and occasional stomach cramps, will have little idea that her symptoms are prompting the homoeopath to mentally flag up potentised onion and strychnine. When, during the consultation, Mary confides that her children sometimes make her so cross she feels like breaking things - it would come as a great shock for her to learn that her *'desire to break things'* is quite possibly bringing potentised scorpion into the clinical picture. At no time in her consultation will Mary have any reason to suspect that anything quite so extraordinary is taking place. However what Mary will notice is that someone at last has time for her, is taking a genuine interest in her situation, asking her questions and generally being a very good listener.

'At last someone is listening to me' is a proven healer in its own right. The relationship developing between Mary and her homoeopath highlights another important factor which must be taken into account when assessing the merit of homoeopathy - that of the placebo effect. Derived from the Latin for 'I will please', the term 'placebo' has been adopted by modern medicine to describe the intangible healing mechanism inherent in the doctor/patient relationship. It is also the term given to any medication which contains no actual medicine but is prescribed to please the patient. The *Concise Medical Dictionary* defines placebo as:

'A medicine that is ineffective but may help to relieve a condition because the patient has faith in its powers.'

The power of the placebo has been known since the beginning of medical history. Socrates wrote:

"I said the cure itself is a certain leaf, but in addition to the leaf there is a certain charm which, if someone chants when he makes use of it, the medicine altogether restores him to health, but without the charm, there is no profit from the leaf [80]*."*

Socrates wrote these words around 420BC. Medical historian S J McMillan tells us that in that same period

"We would be reading prescriptions such as the heel of an Abyssinian greyhound, the tooth of a donkey crushed in honey, not to mention the drugs the leading physicians were compounding out of the bacteria-laden dung of dogs, cats and flies [81]*."*

Considering the all-round lack of medical knowledge and the havoc these revolting prescriptions must have caused, it is amazing the system of patient care known as medicine did not completely collapse, along with the recipients of these nightmarish medications. In fact the opposite was the case - the system positively thrived! In his book, *Pleasing the Patient,* Geoff Watts says:

"It's a testament to the power of the placebo effect that all societies have been prepared to support and even honour men whose medicaments were simply useless if not actually dangerous [82]*."*

There are many books written on the diverse applications of the placebo in modem therapeutic settings. Dr. Samuel Pfeiffer has this to say on the subject:

---

[80] Buckman, Rob & Karl Sabbagh, ibid.
[81] **McMillan, Dr S I** *None of These Diseases*, Oliphants 1967
[82] Watts, Geoff, ibid.

"Approximately thirty to forty percent of all patients respond to placebos very well, while another third do not experience any improvement at all. People who respond well to fake medications are called 'placebo responders'. It is more than coincidence that about the same percentage of patients, one third, show excellent results with acupuncture, homoeopathy, herbal remedies and other unconventional treatments [83]."

Dr Pfeiffer cites this example of two ladies who were separately prescribed the same inert sugar tablet for the same minor condition by the same doctor. The only difference was the manner in which the doctor prescribed each tablet.

"The first lady was told the tablet would alleviate her headache and give her new vigour. The second lady was warned that the tablet was still in its experimental phase, and could possibly cause some unpleasant side effects but it was worth trying anyway. By the next day both patients experienced the symptoms that had been predicted. The first patient felt much better, the other complained of a tingling sensation in the fingertips and slight heartburn [84]."

The differing reactions of the two ladies demonstrate quite clearly that the attitude of the practitioner and the expectations the patient has of their medicine both play a vital part in the process of feeling and getting better.

Physiotherapist Dr A. Kohlrausch says this of reflexology: *"The fact that they are regularly treated over a prolonged period of time is of great significance to many patients. The therapist's active attention gives the patient the comforting feeling that something is actually being done for him. As the therapy has to be applied individually, it undoubtedly has positive aspects, due*

---

[83] Pfeiffer, Dr Samuel, ibid.
[84] Pfeiffer, Dr Samuel, ibid.

to the eminently important contact between patient and therapist achieved through the laying on of hands [85]."

The condensed table below, taken from Rob Buckman's book, *Magic or Medicine,* illustrates very clearly the extent to which the 'practitioner as placebo' effect is given room to exert its influence in Mary's homoeopathic consultation.

Quality	Conventional Doctor	Alternative Practitioner
Time	Usually rushed, average 6 minutes per patient.	Unrushed, average 90 minutes for first consultation - 20 for follow-up.
Emotion Handling	Empathetic abilities are often poor.	Empathetic abilities are often central to the practitioner's skill.
Symptom Handling	Doctors trained to interpret patient's symptoms in the light of knowledge of underlying disease. May disbelieve or contradict patient's view.	Accept patient's symptoms at face value.
Appearance	May appear uncertain. Obliged to express both sides of a controversy.	Usually certain and confident.

It is evident from the table that having time for the patient is a necessary and very important quality. Whilst shortage of time with the patient is unavoidable in the conventional setting, the British Medical Association acknowledges that interpersonal skills in some areas of conventional doctoring are in need of

---

[85] **Kohlrausch, A** *Handbuch der physikalischen Therapie*, Vol II/I, Stuttgart 1971, p.180

improvement. It must be said though that, whatever the nature of these conventional weaknesses, they should not be seen as strengthening the case for homoeopathy. Homoeopathy is being asked to stand as a valid form of medicine in its own right. Before moving on, it would seem suitable at this juncture to set the record straight regarding the aforementioned practice of reflexology.

Reflexology

As always, the true history is very different from the glowing picture portrayed in the current health magazines. Reflexology as we know it today was resurrected from colourful ancient Egyptian ritual and re-vamped in America in the early 20th century by a Dr William Fitzgerald. In a flash of inspiration, Fitzgerald took an anatomical text book, drew all the known human organs, etc. on the bottom of the foot, divided the human body into 10 perpendicular zones, and pronounced a new healing system to the world. Basing the inner workings of his system on the same principles as the *ch'i* and *meridians* in acupuncture, he simply reinvented the packaging. Believing that *vibrational energy* passed through and along these zones, Fitzgerald announced that massaging the patient's foot at specific points would bring relief and healing to the particular organ or bodily appendage, via the manipulation of the *life force* which he believed linked all organs and flowed freely through the said zones. Fitzgerald's followers were assured that enrolling on his inordinately expensive teaching courses would bring the necessary clarity to his confusing mish-mash of therapeutics. When Fitzgerald realised there wasn't enough room to fit all the human body-parts onto the soles of the feet, he expanded his system to include both ankles. Thus it became supposedly possible to treat all organs and all parts of the body, from the brain to the hip, and from wisdom teeth to the intestine.

This whole methodology does demonstrate three recurring themes quite clearly: one, the richness of man's imagination;

two, the endless stream of diverse characters who, down through the centuries, have believed that their discovery alone was the miracle healing system for which the world had been waiting; and three, our ever-exploitable gullibility. In reality, reflexology is absolute nonsense, bearing no relation to anything sensible at all. It's quite ironic to note that in the reflexologists' charts, the actual foot isn't represented. To date, a pain in the foot, according to reflexological thinking, is untreatable.

The Homoeopathic Consultation

Now let us return to placebo, the practitioner/patient interaction and homoeopathy.

As Rob Buckman's table shows, ninety minutes is about right for a first-time homoeopathic consultation. This length of time spent with the patient conveys the impression that the consultation is most thorough and well worth the average fee of fifty pounds. Hahnemann himself listed one hundred questions he believed were necessary to put to the patient in order to arrive at the best possible diagnosis and subsequent remedies. The following extract taken from a modern homoeopathic guide, entitled *Instructions for Patients - How to Communicate Your Case to the Homoeopathic Practitioner*, will give some idea of how the fifty pounds is spent and what the ninety minutes is all about.

"To simply state 'I have a headache'. is too general, but when you add to that statement 'sharp shooting pains in the left side of the head and temple', you simplify the selection of the remedy very much. When you further add 'the pain comes on when the slightest cold air strikes the head' or 'the pains are less when lying down' or 'much worse when walking about' then you state just what the physician needs to guide him. This is called 'individualising the case'. The following suggestions and

questions will aid the patient in giving such a description that the homoeopath may prescribe intelligently.

COUGH AND EXPECTORATION

What kind of cough have you? - *Constant, croupy, crowing, deep, dry, explosive, fatiguing, forcible, frequent, gagging, hacking, jerking, laboured, loose, loud, moist, muffled, nervous, noisy, painful, racking, rapid, rattling, ringing, rough, scraping, screeching, shaking, sharp, short shrill in single coughs, spasmodic, sudden, suffocative, tearing, teasing, tackling, tight, spasmodic, sudden, suffocating, tearing, teasing tight, tormenting, violent, wheezing, whistling.*

What causes the cough? - *anger, anxiety ... laughing.... liver troubles ... least motion... playing the piano... windy weather.*

Do you cough anything up? *What does it taste like? Can you spit it out? Does it fly out of the mouth while coughing? Does it float in water or sink? Is it painful when you cough? What kind of pain is it? Boring, cutting, digging, drawing, dull, gnawing, jerking ... labour-like, oppressive, paralytic, piercing, pinching, pressing, pricking, pulsative, stitching, shooting, tearing, violent?*

Sensations are also important and should be especially noted. It may be like a mouse or bug crawling, as if the heart was grasped by an iron hand, as if claws were grasping the bowels.

Does anything cause the trouble to be worse or better? *It may be reading, writing, music, ascending or descending the stairs, breathing, looking up, down or sideways, excitement, fright, grief, sorrow, fasting, motion or quiet, when nose is discharging or dry, gratification of the passions, before or during* *a thunderstorm, talking, hearing others talking, singing, wet, dry, windy, or cloudy weather.*

The above is given to impress on the mind the great importance of what may seem to be little things. Any one of these may be great or, little, but your physician must be the judge of that.

When does the cough come on? *Early morning, mid-morning, before noon, noon, etc. etc. etc.*[86]

Having some idea of the finer details of this most bizarre approach to the diagnosis and treatment of disease, Dr Mombert's earlier accusations of giddiness and lunacy suddenly don't seem so harsh. This homoeopathic method of reasoning and the knowledge base supporting it has more recently been described by one critic as:

"... the naivest collection of scurrilous scientific rubbish compiled with ingenious good faith that ever appeared in the literature of medicine [87]*."*

And who could disagree?

Armed with some understanding of the history of homoeopathy, of its theory and practice, of the remedies which contain nothing, of the body's amazing capacity to heal itself, and of the healing phenomenon known as the placebo effect, it becomes quite clear that homoeopathy is most definitely **not** the valid form of medicine we are led to believe, and led to believe on such a massive scale! The whole manner in which homoeopathy publicly presents itself, its personalised approach to the patient, the therapeutic setting, the case-taking, the

---

[86] Levenshulme Hom. Clinic, Manchester Waiting room information 1995
[87] Glasscheib, Dr H S, ibid.

76

endless questions, the beautifully illustrated *'materia medicas'* and the computerised repertories - all this is *"...the charm which, if someone chants when he makes use of the medicine, it altogether restores him to health but without the charm there is no profit from the leaf."*

In the same way that homoeopathy never discusses self-limiting illnesses, Geoff Watts notes the scarcity of comment on the charm and power of the placebo effect.

"A skim through the indexes of the collection on my own shelves reveals that references of any kind to placebos or the placebo effect are something of a rarity. Few of these books offer the reader even the slightest hint that there might be questions asked about how and why the methods they describe might actually work [88]."

Self-limiting illnesses and the placebo effect are the unmentioned but vital factors which help maintain homoeopathy's credibility. Demystifying these principles leaves homoeopathy with no credibility whatsoever.

Four hundred years ago, Galileo's detractors argued from their own experience that variable cloud direction and the absence of a constant wind in their faces proved a stationary earth - an assumption now proven to be completely false. In exactly the same manner, today's homoeopaths employ the same faulty reasoning, arguing that their patients' recoveries prove the efficacy of homoeopathy, as evidenced by Andrew Lockie's earlier statement:

"Many homoeopaths are not interested in providing proof because they know from their own experience that it works."

---

[88] Watts, Geoff, ibid.

Yes, we do get better. But as we can now see, not for the reasons the homoeopaths would have us believe. But then the homoeopaths would have us believe a lot of things.

Whilst it is not my intention to belabour the falsity of homoeopathy, it is important to have some idea of the extent to which this respectable and professional-looking industry is actually so remarkably corrupt. It is hoped the next few pages will serve to equip the reader with the discernment necessary to decipher the very convincing fiction that abounds in all homoeopathic writings.

Homoeopathy and The Cholera Effect

Throughout its literature, numerous references are made to homoeopathy's success with more serious illness.

"Homoeopathy became particularly popular in Europe and the United States in the1800's because of its success in treating the epidemics that raged during that time, including cholera, typhoid, yellow fever and scarlet fever [89]."

Dana Ullmann

Homoeopathy's *'success'* in treating scarlet fever and typhoid has already been noted. On the subject of cholera, Andrew Lockie tells his readers:

"A mortality rate of 16.4% was recorded in the homoeopathic hospitals, while the mortality rate was 51.8% in orthodox hospitals. The Board of Health at the time attempted to suppress the damning figures [90]."

At first glance homoeopathy appears much the superior treatment for cholera. Nowhere in his book however does Mr Lockie include any information which might help to set homoeopathy's 'success' into its proper context.

The conventional treatment on offer for cholera at the time included some nightmarish medicaments. Across Europe these poor sufferers were quite regularly subjected to such delights as herbal enemas, sulphuric and nitric acid fumigations, vein cutting, leeches, transfusions of bullock's blood and the ingestion of large amounts of either opium, mercury or turpentine. It was a truly awful affair. The following extract typifies the conventional approach:

---

[89] Ullmann, Dana, ibid.
[90] Lockie, Dr Andrew, ibid.

"By 2.00am she had all the characteristics of Asiatic cholera. The treatment was first a full dose of tincture of opium, with brandy and other stimulants, twenty grains of subchloride of mercury, bleeding from the arm, from which about 2oz of a fluid resembling tar issued. 40oz of weak broth, containing a quantity of saline matter as directed by Dr. Stevens was then thrown into the veins. She expired at 3.00pm [91]."

A certain Dr. Needham treated thirty cholera patients by injecting them with carbonate of soda. Only twenty-six of them died! For these sufferers death was often a merciful relief.

Homoeopathic treatment for the same condition involved no blood letting, purgatives, enemas, turpentine or poisonous fumigations. Very simply, the patient was regularly given one or two drops of camphor diluted beyond existence. More importantly this treatment was administered in a clean and hygienic environment. Of course the mortality rate was lower in the homoeopathic hospitals! But in no way should this be attributed to the clinical effects of homoeopathy, which are nil. The following passage from *The March of Medicine* highlights what is possibly homoeopathy's only contribution to the advancement of medicine, albeit indirect:

"However we may judge Hahnemann's theory, one thing must be admitted. It led to a decisive change in medical thought. Clear-headed doctors realised that a minimum dose of an ineffectual substance, such as homoeopaths used, was tantamount to giving no treatment. If the sick recovered all the same - and this could not be disputed - it must be a matter of self-healing. Homoeopathic treatment - in other words, no treatment - was often far better [92]."

[91] **Shapter, Dr Thomas** *The History of Cholera in Exeter*, S R Publishers 1971
[92] Glasscheib, Dr H S, ibid.

Cholera should not be viewed as a self-limiting illness. It is a very serious condition which is prevented primarily through vaccination. We can be certain though that patients in the homoeopathic hospitals benefited enormously from being spared the brutal ministrations of the orthodox physicians.

And finally on the subject of cholera, this letter dating from 1831, written by a Professor Hufeland to a practising homoeopath, reveals the real reason why, as Mr. Lockie misleadingly puts it, *"...the Board of Health attempted to suppress the damning figures."*

"I wish for nothing more than the truth to be proved in homoeopathy by strictly controlled experiments, including those for cholera. Therefore I wish the homoeopaths had not withdrawn from the supervision of the physicians detailed for that purpose, preventing the verification of their experiences. I now fear that the results obtained will be thought one-sided, prejudiced and unreliable and as such will find very little credence [93]*."*

Time and again there are rational explanations which consistently demonstrate there is actually no link between homoeopathy and cure. This does not stop homoeopaths from asserting that homoeopathy cures and scientifically so.

---

[93] Haehl, Richard, ibid.

The 'Science' of Homoeopathy

"The homoeopathic philosophy or doctrine is a set of rules for practice - one that hasn't changed since it was formulated 180 years ago. These rules and principles constitute a unified hypothesis whose validity is tested out empirically with cured patients confirming the hypothesis [94]."

Miranda Castro

Phew!

With no insight into the true state of affairs concerning homoeopathy, who could not fail to be impressed by Ms Castro's succinct and very scientific-sounding summary? It exudes authenticity. In reality it is thoroughly misleading. Commenting on the pseudo-scientific nature of statements such as *"...cured patients confirming the hypothesis."* Dr Howard Spiro, author of *Doctors, Patients, Placebos,* makes the following observation:

"In his study, The Shaman, which compares shamanistic [occultic] and western methods of healing, Spencer Rogers fails to distinguish between reports of healing and objective evidence of cure. Like most anthropologists, he accepts an 'I feel better' from a person whose headache has been relieved by incantation, as the equal of the same statement by someone cured of pneumonia by penicillin. It is this confusion between the objective and the subjective that characterises so many discussions on healing [95]."

Of the vast number of unfounded claims which homoeopaths make, the statements that irritate the medical establishment most are those which assert that homoeopathy has somehow

---

[94] Castro, Miranda, ibid.

[95] **Spiro, Howard** *Doctors, Patients, Placebos*, Yale University Press 1986

been validated through scientific study and controlled trial. Dana Ullmann's statement typifies the nature of these claims:

"When sceptics today say there is no research on homoeopathy, it is because they have not kept up to date on the latest developments in science and medicine. There are in fact dozens of good scientific studies on homoeopathy. Even when confirming research on homoeopathy is published in respected scientific journals, many conventional physicians will deny the possibility that the medicines actually worked [96]*."*

Once again this is most misleading. What sceptics actually say, and quite correctly so, is that there is very little **good** research taking place. Any research into homoeopathy, which is of sufficient quality, demonstrates repeatedly that homoeopathy has no clinical effect over and above that of placebo.

The British Medical Journal featured an exchange of letters between Dr Rob Buckman and holistic practitioner Dr George Lewith. They were discussing the latest quality trials of homoeopathy. The salient points of their discussion ran as follows:

"Dear George, as I say and as your letter shows, in homoeopathy there are no confirmatory studies. Of the three main randomised studies, two have not been repeated and the last was repeated and did not confirm the initial results. I think you have to agree that at present there are no results of randomised studies which have been successfully repeated and which confirm initial observations, so any clinical effect of homoeopathy over and above that of placebo is not yet proved."

---

[96] Ullmann, Dana, ibid.

"Dear Rob, if the level of proof that you require is repeated studies of the type mentioned, then clearly homoeopathy cannot be seen as a totally proven treatment. However, what remains fascinating is the number of studies with positive results, given the comparative infancy of research in this subject [97]."

While Dr Lewith acknowledges that properly constructed studies of homoeopathy show no positive results, he then goes on to state that he is fascinated by the number of studies that show positive results! This impressive sounding but really very circular style of reasoning dominates so many discussions on homoeopathy today. Dr Lewith's use of the phrase *"...given the comparative infancy of research on this subject"* is really just another way of saying *"The proof lies in tomorrow."*

"Just another way of saying..." is explored in the book, *Opening Pandora's Box*. Authors Gilbert and Mulkay draw attention to the abundance of double-meaning phraseology found in many 'scientific sounding' articles and journals. Some well-worn academic phrases that say one thing but mean another are translated below:

It has long been known that
I haven't bothered to look up the references

Correct within an order of magnitude
Wrong

It appears that
I think

---

[97] *British Medical Journal* Vol. 309, 9th July 1994

It is generally believed
A couple of other guys think so too [98]

Latour and Woolgar take a similarly wry look at these lesser discussed aspects of science in their book, *Laboratory Life*. This next extract reveals how an unqualified observation can so effortlessly don the appearance of scientific fact.

1. The graph shows a series of peaks
2. The patterns of peaks indicate 'X' may be present in 'Y'
3. Smith and Jones studies make it likely 'X' is present in 'Y'
4. 'X' is present in 'Y'

Because 'X' is present in 'Y', we can deduce that ...

References
1 Smith
2 Jones [99]

Employing the same flawed scientific methodology as Hahnemann, Smith and Jones seek no outside validation for their claims and go on to confirm and then publish their own hypothesis. Within this very loose framework are found the *"dozens of scientific studies"* as quoted by Dana Ullmann and *"the studies that show positive results"* as quoted by Dr. George Lewith.

Health and Homoeopathy magazine recently included this report of a clinical trial which took place at the Dynamis School run by homoeopath Jeremy Sherr.

---

[98] **Gilbert & Mulkay** *Opening Pandora's Box*, Cambridge University Press 1984
[99] **Latour & Woolgar** *Laboratory Life*, Princeton University Press 1986

"Various potencies ranging from 6c to 200c were used during the proving as well as a placebo. The proving was undertaken concurrently with hydrogen (6c to 200c) in order to create a double blind trial. The symptoms were checked and re-checked thoroughly to ensure a proving of the highest quality. The proving produced some amazing and truly unexpected results.... Quality provings such as these are essential to the development of our materia medica (database).

Jeremy Sherr and the Dynamis School are in the process of completing the provings of rape seed, germanium, neon and as yet an undisclosed series of substances [100]."

Mr. Sherr's reference to double blind trial needs certain clarification. As stated earlier, properly constructed clinical trials consistently demonstrate that homoeopathy is purely placebo (an inarguable conclusion when acquainted with homoeopathy's true history). It is interesting to note that in his own *'homoeopathically constructed'* trial, Mr Sherr uses placebos in conjunction with two sets of homoeopathic remedies. What this actually means is that Mr Sherr and his team are unwittingly trialing three sets of pills containing nothing at all - a trial which then goes on to produce *"truly unexpected results"*!! Reference to one or two medical facts and scientific terms however lend a degree of respectability to Mr Sherr's report. Paracelsus' indifference to sound methodology was much the same. His scientific approach is elegantly described by his biographer H. Pachter who said of this most unorthodox chemist:

"He bridged inconsistencies by confusing, forgetting, and making up names and by creating special realms where unrelated facts could co-exist without contradiction [101]."

---

[100] **Coghill, Roger** *Electro Healing*, Thorsons 1992
[101] Pachter, H, ibid.

Placebo, double blind, ameliorate, modality and eructation are just a few of the unrelated medical facts and scientific terms used frequently by homoeopathic authors - terms which co-exist quite comfortably in the special realm of homoeopathy. As a footnote, the undisclosed series of substances referred to by Mr Sherr have since been trialed. These substances include yew tree, eagle's blood, salmon, diamond and plutonium!

Brian Inglis gives his readers a few examples of homoeopathic research.

"Orthodox medical and scientific literature abound with examples of which the homoeopaths have gladly availed themselves - that thyroxin can influence the growth of tadpoles, that acetyl chloride can cause a fall in blood pressure when present in proportions of 1mg to 500,000 gallons of blood... that histamine in undetectable quantities provokes reactions in guinea-pigs, and so on. The homoeopaths themselves have evidence that ...[102]" etc., etc.

Mr Inglis gives no sources for this information, bringing us full circle to Mr Lockie's salmon and mercaptan illustrations which, when followed through, were found, just like Inglis' examples, to be wholly irrelevant. This will not stop future authors of homoeopathic works from citing salmon[1], mercaptan[2], tadpoles[3] and 1mg of acetyl chloride to 500,000 gallons of blood[4] as scientific proof of homoeopathy.

References
[1,2] Lockie, Dr Andrew
[3,4] Inglis, Brian

---

[102] Inglis, Brian, ibid.

The Memory of Water and Other Fancies

The clinical trial most frequently referred to by homoeopaths is that of Jacques Benveniste, in which he apparently discovered that water has a memory. According to Benveniste, water can remember something that was in it, but isn't anymore. Was this at last the key to unlocking the mystery of potentisation? A team of independent researchers comprising Dr John Maddox, the editor of *Nature* magazine, a government fraud investigator and James Randi, a psychic claims investigator, requested that Mr Benveniste repeat his experiments under supervision. Mr Benveniste agreed and, not surprisingly, his original results could not be replicated, thus bringing an end to his theory of 'water memory'. Despite Mr Benveniste's failure to repeat his experiments satisfactorily, homoeopaths to this day are still loudly protesting that having 'a magician' (James Randi) on the team of investigators was most unprofessional - an episode which Mr Lockie says:

"...has done little to clarify the issue of potentisation and much to discredit the objectivity and reputation of the orthodox scientific community [103]*."*

This is most unfair. Mr Benveniste was asked to meet only the most basic of criteria. These were to carry out his experiments in exactly the same way as previously done, and to allow a video camera to record the whole procedure. That Mr. Benveniste's experiments failed has nothing whatsoever to do with Mr Randi being present. It merely reminds us once again that Hahnemann's 'less is more' will never be scientifically validated, it being the brainchild of a man wholly immersed in the irrational and occult.

As a passing shot, homoeopath Dana Ullmann argues:

---

[103] Lockie, Dr Andrew, ibid.

"Benveniste was shocked that the 'Nature' team was so biased in their conclusions, especially since their few days of experiments were insignificant compared to his five years of studies [104]*."*

Is it the fault of the *Nature* team that Benveniste spent five years feeling his way meticulously towards a dead end?

Benveniste's latest claim is that he has uncovered 'the language of molecules.' Believing this language to be electromagnetic, Benveniste envisages drugs may soon be sent down the phone, enabling a whole pharmacy to be put on microchip. These claims have led to Mr Benveniste's complete scientific ostracism. His findings have yet to be published in a scientific journal and his laboratory has since been shut down. The BBC2 programme *Heretics* ended with Mr Benveniste wondering aloud whether he should have thrown away his original data. Mr. Benveniste's work is just one example of the *"fairly high powered physics"* referred to earlier by Peter Fisher.

There are scientists who still vigorously defend the Benveniste trials. Among them is Roger Coghill, author of *Electro Healing - Medicine for the Future.* He has put forward some very interesting theories as to why Benveniste could not replicate his experiments:

"What new factors might have upset these delicate experiments?

On the third day, a new dilution was single-coded in front of a video camera. I do not know which camera was used, but a popular model at the time gives off a power frequency electric

---

[104] Ullman, Dana, ibid.

field of 35 volts per metre at three inches in front of its lens. I measured this recently with the appropriate instruments. Benveniste did not suspect the effects of these intrusive fields on the water in his patterned test tubes... apparently the video camera was continually playing, not to mention the electric lights in the room themselves. Finally the squad left with 1,500 photocopies. When these were made and how near the copier was to the experiment is not stated, but since photocopiers emit large quantities of ozone, an unsuitable form of oxygen, it is probable that this too had a devastating effect on the tubes as a result of the huge ion flows generated."

Blaming the failure of Mr. Benveniste's experiments on various emissions from a photocopier, a video camera and some electric strip lights, Mr Coghill then goes on to recommend a laboratory lined entirely with copper which has a window fitted with a sliding gauze panel which can be raised or lowered by means of chains and pulleys.

Mr Coghill asserts:

"Had Benveniste insisted on the same conditions, then the three investigators from 'Nature' would have come back with quite a different story [105]*."*

Mr Coghill goes on to suggest various methods by which mankind might benefit from the use of magnets. These include **'The Cosmotron'**, a pendant about 4.5cm across, marketed in this country by a Mrs H. Pickles of Leeds: *"It concentrates the vital forces of the cosmos within and beams them out to the wearer"* and **'The Rayma Biomagnetic Regulator'**, a metallic bracelet of Spanish manufacture, made of a polarised electrolytic material, which has apparently *"...brought relief to millions in Europe"*. Mr. Coghill has his own invention which he

---

[105] Coghill, Roger, ibid.

promotes as **'The Coghill Supermagnet'**. When applied to the top of the head for two minutes this device is said to improve sexual performance. When applied to the side of the scalp it allegedly improves co-ordination. Apparently **'The Coghill Supermagnet'** can also be used as an intestinal worm control for small mammals. *"Simply apply the magnet to the abdomen of the animal each night for two weeks."*

Mr. Coghill's own ideas that the human brain emits electromagnetic rays has led him to the following conclusion:

"Since men have literally thicker skulls than women, these signals which seem to deteriorate with age have increasing difficulty in reaching the hair follicles on the male head, which is why men are more prone to baldness than women [106]*."*

Homoeopathy's fascination for all things electro-magnetic manifests itself quite bizarrely in the growing practice of electro-diagnostics or radionics - divination by any other name. Until recently, radionics has been the sole domain of another rather dubious therapy, that of naturopathy. Today's radionics apparatus, based loosely on quack Dr. Abraham's infamous 'Black Box' of the 1920's, is supposed to detect mental and physical disharmonies by scanning samples of hair, blood or saliva. Submitting your sample along with a fee of approximately £30.00, the practitioner feeds in the sample, interprets the various signals emitting from an impressive array of dials, gauges and winking lights, and then returns the verdict, along with the appropriate remedy. Sceptics wishing to determine the sensibility of the snaking electrics contained in these little boxes are invariably told that removing the back upsets the delicate nature of the instruments. One firm, South West Radionics Association, told me I would not understand the full significance of the internal workings without a complete grasp of radionics

---

[106] Coghill, Roger, ibid.

theory and a background in quantum mechanics.

Even more significant however is the large number of sceptics who, over the years and unbeknownst to these practitioners, have submitted samples of blood, hair or saliva of **non-human** origin for a radionic reading. Quack medical histories abound with glorious examples of situations where these rogue operators have inadvertently revealed the true worth of their radionics boxes. In one instance, the saliva of a young cow returned the verdict of *"an inordinate interest in women"*. In another, a reading taken from the blood of a rooster prompted the practitioner to pronounce the root of the patient's problem as *"suffering from bad teeth and a sinus infection.*[107]*"*

In his chapter 'Dowsing for Homoeopathic Remedies', homoeopath Arthur Bailey freely confesses that a near absence of wiring within these homoeopathic dowsing instruments leaves one slightly nonplussed as to their operation, but maintains an adamant stance that *"...nevertheless they do seem to work."* Mr Bailey goes on to cite the following example as validation of his dowsing methods:

Whilst with a group of friends in a non English-speaking Italian restaurant, the party was having considerable difficulty deciding what to order from an otherwise unintelligible menu. Tongue in cheek, his sceptical friends suggested to Mr Bailey that he might use his dowsing skills to determine the most flavoursome dish. Mr Bailey rose unflinchingly to the challenge:

"I got out my pendulum and dowsed down the incomprehensible list. One item in particular gave a very strong

---

[107] Pfeiffer, Samuel. *ibid*

reaction. Taking courage in both hands, I ordered it. When it came, the sceptics were silenced. I had ordered by far the best item on the menu. It was delicious [108]*."*

This brief glimpse into the science, facts and figures of homoeopathy brings a much-needed perspective to announcements such as *"Scientists and speakers from all over the world gathered for the 23rd Annual Homoeopathic Convention."*

In determining to prove that homoeopathic remedies contain 'something', homoeopathic scientists fall into the trap known as experimenter's regress. This term is well illustrated by the following example, albeit from a different field of scientific enquiry, determining the existence of gravity waves.

"The correct outcome of a gravity wave detection experiment depends upon whether there are gravity waves hitting the earth in detectable fluxes. To find this out we must first build a good gravity wave detector and have a look. But we will not know if we have built a good detector until we have tried it and obtained a correct outcome. But we don't know what the correct outcome is until....[109]*"* and so on, and so on, ad infinitum.

How does one successfully build a machine to detect that which might not even exist in the first place?

---

[108] Wallace. 'Anyone Can Dowse For Better Health' Quantum Books 1999
[109] *Research Methodology*, UMIST course hand-out 1994

The Ethics of Homoeopathic Research

In an effort to maintain credibility before the critical gaze of orthodox science, a great deal of time and money is being wasted on the creation of homoeopathic 'micro dose detection' experiments. Homoeopathic 'scientists' must be seen to be hunting for something that in reality is completely non-existent.

The repeated failure to detect anything even remotely active in homoeopathic remedies does not bring the theory of 'less is more' crashing down, as it should. On the contrary, it merely opens the way for bigger and better regressive experiments, with bigger and better detectors as this snippet from *Health and Homoeopathy* sadly, but not unsurprisingly confirms:

"The memory of water has since surfaced again.... A co-ordinated series of further experiments with improved methods are in progress in the US, Northern Ireland, Italy, France and the Netherlands. Watch this space..."

The ethics of this whole affair are justified by the homoeopathic industry's vague assurance that *"the research is in its infancy.."* etc. etc.

On the subject of medical ethics, Stuart Pocock, author of *Clinical Trials*, writes:

"One basic premise is that it is unethical to conduct research which is badly planned or poorly executed. That is, if a trial is of sufficiently poor quality that it cannot make a meaningful contribution to medical knowledge, then it should be declared unethical [110]*."*

---

[110] **Pocock, Stuart** *Clinical Trials*, Wiley 1983

Searching for an active principle in homoeopathic remedies makes no meaningful contribution to medical knowledge. There is no active principle in the remedies. Homoeopaths who corner conventional medical science for the purposes of validating their experiments are draining these conventional agencies of valuable resources which could otherwise be put to better and more ethical use.

In the very latest respectable orthodox report on homoeopathic trials, released in January 1999, Professor Ernst from the Department of Complementary Medicine at Exeter University makes the following observations:

"It is interesting to note that the mostly commercially sponsored trials tended to yield positive results hinting at the possibility of strong sponsor bias.
Only few comparative trials of homoeopathy exist. None is free from serious methodological flaws. Thus the value of homoeopathy relative to allopathic medicine is unknown."

How many more reports, biased or otherwise are needed to ascertain the value of homoeopathy? Its value is not unknown. Homoeopathy is completely valueless!

Let us hope that Professor Ernst's time consuming **'Perfusion 12: 13-15'** report is his last on homoeopathy. There are surely many agendas of far more importance which would benefit from his valuable input.

Veterinary Homoeopathy

The last remaining area of homoeopathic practice to examine is that of veterinary homoeopathy. In discussing the placebo effect with homoeopaths, a point is always reached where they say *"If you're suggesting homoeopathy relies on placebo, then how do you explain homoeopathy's success with animals?"*

In his book, *Alternative Medicine*, Andrew Stanway says:

"Homoeopathic remedies have been used to excellent effect in animals. This is a good answer to those who feel there is a large placebo action in homoeopathy [111]."

Discussing these statements with the various authors it soon becomes apparent that very few of them have actually looked up any references to support their statements. The prevailing perception that veterinary homoeopathy is effective is influenced in the main by the plethora of very convincing articles currently doing the rounds in the popular press. Here is a good example taken from *Health Guardian*, a natural health products magazine:

"Homoeopathy is becoming a very popular therapy for animals of all kinds. A growing number of vets are turning to this gentle, safe and effective treatment ...Virtually any condition can be treated with homoeopathic remedies - chronic problems unresponsive to conventional drugs - such as dermatitis, bronchitis and rheumatism - are especially well-suited to the deep-healing action of homoeopathy. **Many pets pronounced incurable by conventional drugs have shown an amazing improvement with homoeopathy [112]."**

---

[111] Stanway, Dr Andrew, ibid.
[112] **Allport, Richard** *Health Guardian*, May 1992

I contacted the homoeopathic vet who wrote the article in order to discuss these very specific claims - in particular, *"the amazing improvements"* highlighted in bold above. Quite incredibly, he could offer no evidence at all to support any of his claims. He agreed with me that the article was misleading and stated:

"The successes referred to in the article are all anecdotal. You cannot really show that homoeopathy has actually had any effect."

This article is more than just misleading, it breaks just about every ethical reporting code going. However, its inclusion in the widely read *Health Guardian* can only have bolstered homoeopathy's false reputation as an effective form of animal treatment.

Much consulted homoeopathic vet Tim Couzens, who writes the 'Help for Pets' page in *Here's Health* would answer no questions on any aspect of his practice. He told me:

" I'm sorry, but I cannot answer any of your questions. It is a policy decision not to offer information. It makes my life much more simple if I don't get involved."

At the time of writing, Christopher Day is the secretary of the British Association of Homoeopathic Veterinary Surgeons and is recognised as the leading authority in veterinary homoeopathy. He has written a number of books on the subject, and has also appeared in a very misleading video entitled *Homoeopathy - A Realistic Alternative*. In one particular scene, Mr Day was filmed administering a few drops of a homoeopathic remedy to a cow suffering from milk fever.

Shot of Mr Day in cow shed.

Narrator: *"From race horses to a dairy herd is all in a day's work. The patient today is a cow with milk fever."*

Mr. Day: *"We're left with the fact that there is a milk fever problem. She's already had the calcium injections but it hasn't completely worked. So what we're going to do is see if homoeopathic remedies can restore the balance for her."*

Mr. Day administers the drops.

Narrator: *"In less than an hour the cow showed a remarkable improvement.... and it soon became apparent why this farmer had entrusted his cows to Chris Day's homoeopathic medicine* [113]*."*

Closing shot of cow, looking sleek and healthy.

As ever, there is a good reason why all this appears so very convincing. Milk fever is caused by a fall in the level of blood calcium. The only way to treat this condition is by the intravenous injection of large amounts of replacement calcium. With the calcium deficiency rectified, the cow is usually back on its feet between half an hour and six hours after the injection.

With these facts in mind I wrote to Mr Day suggesting that his treatment did not actually confirm the efficacy of homoeopathy. I noted in my letter that the cow had first been given the necessary conventional treatment. This was then followed by the homoeopathic treatment. Moreover the homoeopathic treatment had been administered by Mr Day well within the time period expected for the conventional treatment to have its effect.

---

[113] *Homoeopathy: A Realistic Alternative*, ibid.

Surely it was a case of the conventional treatment doing all the work and homoeopathy getting the credit.

Mr Day answered none of these questions, replying only:

"Thank you for your facsimile message. I am not responsible for the video. I advise you to contact the company who made it. I trust they will be able to help you. "

On speaking to Materia Medica, the company which produced the video, they pointed out that explaining Mr Day's methods was not their responsibility. Quite right too. Repeated attempts to contact Mr. Day eventually resulted in a very brief conversation. He would offer no information on any of his treatments and, when questioned over his milk fever remedy coinciding with the calcium injection, he replied:

"The cow needed balancing anyway."

This typifies the quality of evidence supporting veterinary homoeopathy. In short, there isn't any. One orthodox vet who worked closely with a homoeopathic vet over a twelve-month period told me:

"In that time I did not see one instance that demonstrates that homoeopathy cured animals."

Once again, just as in human homoeopathy, it is self-limiting illness and homoeopathic treatment coinciding with the necessary conventional treatment which accounts for the entire spectrum of homoeopathy's success with animals.... that and a very liberal dose of wildly inaccurate reporting!

Hahnemann's Latter Years

What of Hahnemann? Now in his sixties, his years of poverty and hardship were over at last. He was revelling in his new-found success. It did not of course occur to homoeopathy's founder that his patients' recoveries had nothing to do with his remedies. On the contrary, Hahnemann's business success only confirmed to him that homoeopathy was the divine medicine he'd always said it was. He took his success as a sign to go forth and preach his beloved homoeopathy, which he referred to as *"the only true medicine"*. His address to a gathering of medical students in Paris began:

"I am come into France for the propagation of Homoeopathy.... and to you, studious young Frenchmen, so that the old ways may not encompass you. Come to me, for I will impart to you that truth much sought for ... I am nothing but a feeble instrument of that Majesty before which all should humiliate themselves [114]*."*

Assuming his role as the messiah of medicine, Hahnemann wrote unceasingly to his growing following of 'true disciples', as he called them, instructing them on *'the truths'* to be found in homoeopathy. He had his portrait struck on medallions, rings and pendants, which he enclosed in his letters, and he commissioned sculptors to make busts of himself, for his followers to display in their own homes.

Hahnemann settled in Paris and set up practice. It wasn't long before the rich and famous were queuing at the door of the miracle-working physician now residing at No.1, Rue de Milan. This extract from the diary of a famous actress at the time,

---

[114] Bradford, Thomas, ibid.

Anua Mowatt, describes her visit to the salon of the celebrated Dr Hahnemann:

"See, there is Dr. Hahnemann's house!" the coachman replied, pointing to a palace-like mansion. I leaned out of the window and beheld a long line of carriages in front of us, driving one by one through the gates. Behind us stretched a line of coaches, lengthening every minute.... all coming to pay homage to this modern Aesculapius.

My carriage deposited me at the front entrance of Hahnemann's magnificent dwelling. The salon was occupied by fashionably dressed ladies and gentlemen and children with their nurses. I examined the fine paintings, the sculptures, the costly vases and the number of curious looking medals heaped upon a centre table....

Every room contained several marble busts of Hahnemann, some much larger than life, some as large and some smaller. These also had been presented to him on different occasions as tokens of respect. I was standing before a most life-like portrait of the great doctor, lost in admiration of its masterly execution.... A glance at the clock informed me it was some three hours since I first entered the house.... The valet announced that Monsieur le Docteur was ready to receive me. Throwing open the door he loudly announced me and retired.... I stood in the presence of Monsieur le Docteur and Madame Hahnemann [115]."

Following the same career paths, and reaching the same dizzy levels of notoriety as our old friends, the 'Count de St Germaine', and the 'hockogrockle' vendors, Hahnemann was now netting over two hundred thousand francs a year, having

---

[115] Bradford, Thomas, ibid.

found fame and fortune at last. However, his methods were becoming increasingly bizarre. Hahnemann suddenly announced that smelling his remedies cured illnesses more effectively than swallowing them:

"Not only can I obtain mastery over the severest cases of chronic disease by letting the patient smell my medicines, but I can do so in an incredibly short space of time [116]*."*

Hahnemann listed breast cancer, deafness, herpes, crooked spines, tuberculosis and suicidal tendencies amongst the illnesses he believed were curable by this method:

"A man whose one thought is suicide, even if he only inhales once from this small bottle, will abhor his intended purpose and will return to a calm state of mind, with a desire to live [117]*."*

From 'healing by smelling', Hahnemann moved on to mesmerism and animal magnetism. This next text gives some idea of the 'mesmeric' truths Hahnemann was propagating to his disciples:

"The most spectacular cures are brought about by men who, bursting with vital energy, use their extremely strong and benevolent will to transmit human force to the entire organism and revive someone who has apparently been dead for some time. Especially if those men have only the slightest sexual desire or none at all. The subtle life energies used in the production of semen are available in them and ready to be communicated by strength of will through touch to others [118]*."*

---

[116] Haehl, Richard, ibid.
[117] Haehl, Richard, ibid.
[118] Hahnemann, Christian Samuel, ibid.

It was this period in Hahnemann's life that prompted his biographer Richard Haehl to politely comment:

" [His thinking] *led him finally to courses which even in his lifetime divided him from a great number of his adherents, and which were largely abandoned by his later disciples as not belonging to the realms of science and pure therapy* [119]."

The young and beautiful Melanie d'Hervilly, Hahnemann's second wife and the business brain behind the Hahnemann empire, was able to keep her husband's ideas from becoming too prominent in his surgeries. But already there were whispers that the old doctor from Germany *'wasn't very well.'*

What of his family? Right from the very beginning Hahnemann had involved his whole family in his experiments. An acquaintance of the family wrote:

"A very peculiar mode of life prevailed in Hahnemann's house. The members of his family, the patients and students lived and moved in only one idea and that was homoeopathy. His daughters assisted in the preparation of his medicines and gladly took part in the provings. Patients enthusiastically celebrated the effects of homoeopathy and devoted themselves as apostles to spread the fame of the new doctrine among unbelievers.

All who adhered to Hahnemann were the butt of ridicule or objects of hatred. But so much more did the homoeopathists hold together like members of a persecuted sect hanging with more exalted reverence and love upon their honoured head – Hahnemann [120]."

---

[119] Haehl, Richard, ibid.
[120] Bradford, Thomas, ibid.

Hahnemann's household was no ordinary household. It bore all the hallmarks of a cult of which he was the leader, ruling with a rod of iron.

"If anyone deviates from my teachings by one hair's breadth, he is a traitor with whom I shall have nothing to do! [121] *"*

Hahnemann's family grew up in this rigid environment, serving their leader with unquestioning obedience. This fearful way of life exacted a price. When Hahnemann moved to Paris, he left his house in Kothen, Germany to his two daughters. A visitor to their gloomy abode remarked:

"The two sisters went to bed for a few hours in the day time while they passed the nights fully dressed in an armchair for fear that something evil might happen to them. In the room that had once been Hahnemann's consulting room, a bell-pull had been installed, and at night the two daughters rang the big harsh bell on the landing in turn, every hour to show they were still awake [122] *."*

Hahnemann died in 1843 aged eighty-eight. Before he died, he made arrangements for his tomb to be engraved with the epitaph '*Non Inutilis Vixi*' which, with typical Hahnemann modesty, translates '*I have not lived in vain*'.

Of his eleven children, one died at birth, one died aged two, another aged thirty, two were murdered in mysterious circumstances, one went insane and disappeared, the others lost contact with their father, including the two daughters most loyal to him, who had decided to stay behind in the old house in Kothen. It was Hahnemann's son Friedrich who went insane and

---

[121] Haehl, Richard, ibid.
[122] Haehl, Richard, ibid.

vanished. He left behind a wife and child. One biographer wrote of this sad affair:

"Friedrich emptied onto his family the cup of demonism with which his father had endowed him [123]*."*

---

[123] Pfeiffer, Dr Samuel, ibid.

Homoeopathy and its Influence Today

"As you sow, so shall you reap." So read the immortal words of scripture. The seeds of 'similia similibus' and 'less is more' and other errant philosophies grew like strangling weeds in the minds and lives of Hahnemann and his family. Today there are critics of homoeopathy who dismiss its principles as nonsensical, yet still believe the therapy has a useful role to fulfil. Paraphrased, their arguments can be summarised as follows:

"OK, so there's a bit of mumbo-jumbo, and we know homoeopathy relies on placebo. But if the patient is not at risk and happy at the end of the day, what's the fuss? Alongside conventional medicine, homoeopathy is much cheaper and demand for the remedies is creating employment opportunities, thus contributing to the economy. All in all there are a lot worse things going on in the world. Rather than coming down so hard on homoeopathy, let's get to grips with the bigger issues: pollution, the arms race, etc., etc."

Donald Gould, the former editor of *New Scientist*, warns of the dangers we invite by adopting such laissez-faire reasoning.

"Why not make the most of what the non-conformists have to offer and to hell with uncharitable logic? There is, I suggest, a powerful reason for rejecting this superficially attractive option. Truth is a fundamental value. If we accept uncritical thinking in one area of our lives for the sake of convenience or because of the popular appeal of a seductive myth and the short-term comfort to be gained by believing in the unbelievable, or because the false answer lets us pretend we are competently coping with a painful problem we haven't truly tackled, then we are all the more likely to adopt the same strategy in other situations, from dealing with the family, to managing the national

economy, and from chairing the parish council to handling arsenals of nuclear weapons. The result is likely to be unhappy and stands a decent chance of proving a disaster. Irrational beliefs are always dangerously corrupting, even when they only relate to the cause and cure of piles [124]*."*

There is no doubt that homoeopathy is contributing to the economy. Annual expenditure on homoeopathic products throughout Europe exceed £590 million. It is estimated there are 1,200 registered homoeopathic practitioners in the UK and, according to some sources, as many again who are unregistered and currently doing business. There are five homoeopathic hospitals in the UK - London, Bristol, Liverpool, Glasgow and Tunbridge Wells.

The London hospital sees an average of five hundred patients a week and all the hospitals report growing interest in their services. A growing number of GPs now include homoeopathy on the list of treatments they wish to see more widely available on the National Health Service. The Faculty of Homoeopathy reports homoeopathy as the fastest growing therapy today and Boots the Chemist now trains its staff in the rudiments of homoeopathy to meet the growing public demand for information on the remedies.

As interest in homoeopathy continues to grow, less and less does there appear to be any debate highlighting the grim realities fundamental to this therapy. The talk today seems to focus only on bringing a professional sheen to homoeopathic practice. The Medical Control Agency, which supervises the retail of medicines in this country, is insisting on standard conditions, such as uniform registration schemes for homoeopaths, uniform manufacturing methods for the remedies and more specific information to be displayed on the labels.

---

[124] **Gould, Donald** *The Black and White Medicine Show*, Hamilton 1985

Representing the homoeopathic industry, homoeopath Peter Fisher has stated: *"Harmonisation of training and regulation of practitioners is the challenge of the future [125]."* Once again, their lines of reasoning are scratching only the surface of the issue.

And what of the homoeopaths to be who, at this present time, are spending their hundreds of pounds at the numerous homoeopathic colleges, soaking up all of Hahnemann's meticulously compiled nonsense - the endless repertories, including the latest homoeopathic work, *Repertorium Homoeopathicum Syntheticum,* the case-taking training, *Hering's Law of Cure, typologies, constitutional prescribing, miasms, psora* and a hundred more homoeopathic idiosyncrasies? And what worth can we really attach to the following homoeopathic titles and qualifications: L.C.H., M.C.H., R.S.Hom., Dip.Hom(Med), M.F.Hom. etc. etc.? Just what is it these students are swallowing?

In his commentary on some of the root causes of social problems, W. Deutscher very clearly encompasses the *problem* of homoeopathy, with these telling and universally applicable words:

"We concentrate on consistency without much concern of what it is we are being consistent about, or whether we are consistently right or wrong. As a consequence, we have been learning a great deal about how to follow an incorrect cause with the maximum of precision [126]"

So why aren't there a whole host of books out there, telling us about the gaping holes in this alternative business? Why is homoeopathy only *'good news'* ? Some well-known and influential publishing houses read the manuscript for this book.

---

[125] *British Medical Journal*, Vol. 309, ibid.

[126] **Deutscher** *Social Problems*, UMIST course hand-out, ibid.

They told me they liked the work and found the subject matter interesting. But in almost every case, I was told that to publish my book would be to compromise their position with current authors. Currently earning enormous sums of money from books actively promoting the various alternative therapies, one senior editor I spoke to was quite forthright: *"Look, it's just that our readers love a good fairy tale."* But not the truth, it seems.

WHICH Publications, the eyes and ears of today's consumer market, rejected this manuscript, stating that they were soon to be releasing their own book, the authoritatively titled *Which Guide to Complementary Medicine*. With their volume already typeset and the presses ready to roll, the *Which* editorial team told me quite testily: *"Our guide deals quite effectively with the subject at hand."* The following extract is taken from their chapter *'dealing effectively'* with homoeopathy:

"...but it was a German doctor, Samuel Hahnemann, who established the principle for the modern world.... sickened by orthodox brutality, he abandoned his flourishing practice..... discovered that Peruvian bark produced in himself all the symptoms of malaria.... and as a result he published his Law of Similars in 1796...etc. etc."

BUPA's Spring '99 edition of their quarterly magazine *Upbeat - The Amazing Way to Health* includes numerous health-related articles of varying accuracy. The BUPA article on homoeopathy warrants special mention, especially so, when one considers the influence and stature of this highly respected organisation. With a flourishing *"We tell you about the healing power of homoeopathy,"* the article condenses thus: *"Hahnemann, dissatisfied with the crude practice of the time, sought a gentle alternative. Based on the law of similars, he used natural ingredients and modern homoeopathy was born. Healing according to 'like cures like', some conditions mean you might see the homoeopath only every couple of months, other more immediate problems, you may need to make a visit every few days."*

The following 'natural ingredients' are then recommended: **silver nitrate** for anxiety, a blend of **lime of oyster shell** and **sulphur** for sore throats, **liquid mercury** for swollen glands, **sea sponge** for coughs, and **St John's Wort** for *'injuries to nerve-rich parts of the body.'* BUPA advise their members that consultation fees range from £35-£100 per session and that reimbursement for treatments such as these is dependant on using *'only BUPA-recognised homoeopaths.'* An 0845 number is included at the end of the article to secure the services of said practitioners.

It really is quite breath-taking! In attempting to summarise the above, one is reminded of Captain Blackadder's forthright appraisal of Baldrick's epic poem: *"War's a terrible thing, ding-a-ling-a-ling".* Enduring the rendition quite magnificently, Blackadder concludes: *"Well.... it started off badly, it tailed off a little towards the middle, and the less said about the end the better. But apart from that, excellent!"*

Just what is going on? Somewhere down the line, something seems to have gone horribly wrong. If truth is a fundamental value, and I believe it is, then surely there should be no place in our society for the irrational, corrupting myths that constitute homoeopathy and homoeopathic practice. *"Harmonisation of training and regulation of practitioners.... "established the principle for the modern world.."* and *"..using only BUPA recognised homoeopaths etc., etc."* is all just building on sand! The extent to which homoeopathy has settled so comfortably into our society is indicative of a much deeper malaise. One must ask, "What on earth has happened to our thinking?" More to the point, in and amongst this holistic jungle, "What on earth is happening to us?"

Doctors now say that upwards of seventy percent of their patients may be visiting them for stress-related conditions. These same doctors are finding themselves under intense pressure to manage their ever-increasing caseloads. In a survey conducted by *BMA News Review*, 88% of doctors believed their patients were being encouraged to make unreasonable demands on their services. 69% of doctors had themselves suffered from stress-related conditions, and 70% of doctors believed the stress they were experiencing was directly affecting their work. The article included the following observation:

"*Increasing patient numbers, the constant worry about being sued, the Patient's Charter, and sensationalist and incorrect media coverage add an enormous amount of pressure to an already busy, stressful and very responsible job. Doctors need protecting from the totally unrealistic expectations of patients and their families, as well as from an increasing spiral of litigation* [127]."

With divorce rates going through the roof, teenage sex and pregnancy on the increase, abortion on demand, general morality decreasing, and general criminality escalating, there's more than enough stress to go around. We are suffering from an ill for which the doctor has no pill. It seems we need more than just physical repair. And when we add to these woes the everyday stories of world-wide political conniving, pollution, famine, wars and disasters, is it any wonder that many of us begin to look for a more meaningful, perhaps more *spiritual* way of life?

---

[127] *BMA News Review* April 1996

Enter the Slippery Magicians

Our 'toxic hopelessness', as it has been described, and our subsequent demand for *instant* spiritual fulfillment, has opened the door to a whole host of 'hockogrockle' alternative New Age merchants. This next extract is taken from a recent promotional poster. Plastered liberally across inner London, the posters were fanfaring the imminent arrival to our shores of Deepak Chopra, new age guru and inner healer. Currently earning millions in America, Deepak was now heading this way with his own particular, and I think, particularly unwholesome false gospel:

"We all need to be healed in the highest sense, by making ourselves perfect in mind, body and spirit. The first step is to realize that this is even possible. The power asleep in us all doesn't awaken until we call."

As with many New Spirituality/New Age promises, the listener is soothingly told that 'perfection' lies within each of us. We are also told that Mr Chopra is in possession of a *'secret formula'* known only to him. And this secret formula, we are assured, will *'awaken our inner perfection'*. But just like old Hahnemann's 'secret' scarlet fever remedy, which was a) available only by paying for it in advance, and b) completely useless, Mr Chopra's own particular snake oil for *'all emptinesses known to mankind'* is ours, only upon receipt of a considerable amount of money up front, and, in terms of combating the said *emptiness*, will be equally useless.

George Vithoulkas, well respected in homoeopathic circles and a prolific writer on the subject, is equally convinced that we have it within us to overcome all the ills known to man - that we can infact heal ourselves. In his book *Homoeopathy, Medicine for the New Man,* Vithoulkas considers the following philosophical instruction to be a vital ingredient to the teachings of all homoeopathic colleges:

*"Finally, the teachings of the school should be such as to bring about in the very depths of the students' hearts **the realisation that mankind's destiny is to free itself from the bondages of pain, of passion and of selfishness**[128]."*
(bold italics mine)

These students then go on to become our indoctrinated homoeopaths. In turn, these homoeopaths then begin to teach us, either subliminally but in main quite openly, that the power to heal ourselves is within us, that we can free ourselves from our current physical, mental, even spiritual predicaments.

Whilst a positive attitude is a valuable weapon to possess in the fight against illness, this particular philosophical stance often carries a very unhealthy flip side. The *'we can heal ourselves'* mantra is just one of many damaging *alternatives* being irresponsibly preached to the more seriously ill. I have spoken to many people where the shared experience is one of eventually realising they were riding the never-ending alternative merry-go-round, being passed from one therapist to another, always at great financial cost, with physical and mental cost very often an added extra.

This scenario is quite accurately summed up thus: *"Well Mary, we have exhausted every avenue with our particular approach, and it seems we are no longer able to help you. However, there may well be a way forward here. May I suggest that you visit my colleague, Dr X, Y, Z, Dip.Hom., N.I.M.H., D.O., M.C.T., etc., etc.? It is probable that in this instance you require*

---

[128] **Vithoulkas, George** *Homoeopathy, Medicine for the New Man*, Thorsons 1985

a deeper healing than can be offered with just homoeopathy. Please do try Dr X, Y, Z. Here is his card. I've heard he produces excellent results."

Feeling that it is somehow her fault for continuing to feel unwell, for not possessing sufficient *'inner wisdom'* to heal herself, Mary heads off to the next equally expensive therapist, determined to battle on, but inwardly all the more despondent. Her previous therapist has contributed nothing to her situation, except perhaps in terms of adding more confusion.

There are literally thousands of self-appointed therapists/spiritual advisers in business today, most of whom operate outside any sensible regulatory control. It is perhaps this 'rogue operator' aspect of Alternative Health that has the capacity to be so damaging, especially when it filters down into organisations we know and trust. The following leaflet was left in a local Citizen's Advice Bureau:

"Did you know homoeopathy can help you through any trauma or crisis? £15.00 for a half-hour appointment. For enquiries and appointments with our acute trauma clinic, please telephone 01424 ——————."

New Age...?

In her book, *Gods of the New Age,* author Caryl Mastrisciana details her many years' involvement in New Age practices and also the reasons for her subsequent exit from the movement. Citing the near absence of spiritual guidelines or conditions, the New Age movement's almost universal avoidance of real-life issues and its general lack of teaching on morality and personal accountability, Caryl gathers together these and a few other rather undemanding ingredients to present her recipe for New Age cake:

2 cups of hope (carefully sift out all fear)
2 cups of altered consciousness (yoga, drugs or meditation to taste)
3 tablespoons each of self awareness, self-improvement and self-esteem (be sure to melt away anything negative)
1 heaped teaspoon of peace
1 large dollop of love
1 generous pinch each of humanism, eastern mysticism and occultism
1 handful of holism
1 scoop of mystical experience
Mix thoroughly together
Bake in a warm friendly environment
Fill with your most appealing dreams
Garnish generously with positive thoughts and good vibrations [129].

Now, while the world is no doubt in full agreement with the idea of *"large dollops of love"*, what room have we made for good old-fashioned moral and intellectual integrity? History has amply demonstrated that a society not confronting the reality of its amoral behaviour, its 'anything-goes' attitudes and general waywardness, is a society that has begun the inevitable descent to disaster. And whilst we can permit ourselves a wry grin at Caryl's New Age cake recipe, it is not so light a matter that millions of us continue with beliefs which appear harmless enough on the surface, but which have proven, time and time again, to draw the unwary ever deeper into the occult, as we saw with Samuel Hahnemann and others of his day.

Not a very nice place to end up, you'll agree.

---

[129] **Mastriciana, Caryl** *Gods of the New Age,* Harvest House Publishers, 1985

Complementary?

Some readers may have noted that throughout this book I have referred to homoeopathy and its counterparts as *alternative*, and not *complementary*. This is simply because the facts prove that in the main, these therapies **do not** complement our overall health. If we adopt the principles of investigation, as outlined in this study of homoeopathy, and lay them as a straight stick against the claims heralded by the other major therapies, it soon becomes apparent that reflexology, iridology, flower remedies, naturopathy, almost all herbalism, and a host more alternative 'treatments' fall dismally short of the claims they themselves espouse.

Yes, our modern day pharmacopaeia is 70% plant-based, and there are many plants and plant derivatives in use today, arresting and/or reversing disease, bringing relief of one kind or another to many otherwise suffering individuals. And yes, we can also find well-meaning alternative health practitioners advising us to diet, sleep, exercise and generally look after ourselves more effectively. But is this sensible approach to healthcare solely the monopoly of holism? Of course not! And when these generalities are stripped from the alternative practitioners' 'modus operandi', there is precious little left that could be considered conducive to our general health and well-being. In the main, what is left serves only to trick and dazzle the unsuspecting mind. Fortunately, there has now been a fundamental shift in this whole equation. You now have a straight stick in your hand, and you can measure the therapies for yourself.

The Best Medicine!

It has never been the aim of this book to present an in-depth study of the failings of society, or of the failings, or otherwise, of our current healthcare providers, or of the nature of illness and recovery! Neither has it been the aim of this book to present a running commentary on the tennis played between the BMA, the National Health Service and alternative health, or on the politics governing these issues. It is my hope that this book has helped to cut a clear path through the thick and thorny undergrowth which so notoriously bedevils the whole subject of alternative health.

But more than this, I hope that *'What Are We Swallowing?'* has enabled the reader to develop the discernment necessary to unravel the wider and more serious issue of crooked thinking. Having a grasp of the issues raised thus far, it is my firm conviction we will then be able to battle much more effectively for that very healthiest of medicines - not only for the benefit of ourselves as individuals, but for our society as a whole - the refreshing, revitalising, restorative medicine of truth!

Let us end as we began, and leave the last word to Oliver Cromwell. Of the thousands of books and magazines sold in our bookshops, libraries and newsagents the length and breadth of our land, all of which paint such flattering portraits of homoeopathy and other alternative therapies - to these artists and their art, our plain-speaking, plain-looking friend would have undoubtedly remarked:

"Sirs, 'tis plain. A true likeness of this most unbecoming subject you have not captured in any way. As such, these works, for all their flattery, are not worth a single farthing."

Bibliography & References

AUTHORS

Allport, Richard *Health Guardian*, May 1992 96
Bambridge, A D *Homoeopathy - Results Beyond Reason*, 1992...........................44
Bellamy, David *Blooming Bellamy*, BBC Books 1993...40
Bradford, Thomas *Life and Letters of Samuel Hahnemann*, Jain Publishers 192114, 33, 100, 101, 103
Brand, Dr Paul *The Forever Feast*, Monarch Publications 1994 56
Brunton, Dr Nelson *Homoeopathy*, Optima 1989...54, 62
Camp, John *The Healer's Art*, F Muller 1978 29
Campbell, Anthony *Natural Health Handbook*, QED Books 1991 48
Castro, Miranda *Complete Homoeopathy*, MacMillan Press 1990...................60, 82
Coghill, Roger *Electro Healing*, Thorsons 1992...86, 90, 91
Constable, Nick *Fated Destiny*, Blitz Editions 1994 18
Dwyer, Dr John *Body at War*, Unwin Hyman 1988...57
Finigan, Peter *The Natural Therapies A-Z*, Thorsons 1994 8
Gilbert & Mulkay *Opening Pandora's Box*, Cambridge University Press 1984.......85
Glasscheib, Dr H S *The March of Medicine*, McDonald & Co 1963 ....45, 76, 80
Gould, Donald *The Black and White Medicine Show*, Hamilton 1985 107
Haehl, Richard *Samuel Hahnemann - His Life and Work*, Jain Publishers 19719, 14, 15, 19, 21, 22, 23, 25, 27, 33, 34, 37, 40, 45, 81, 102, 103, 104
Hahnemann, Christian Samuel *Organon of Medicine*, Gollancz 198624, 42, 51, 52, 102
Hamill, John & R A Gilbert *World Freemasonry*, Aquarian Press 1991 12
Hammond, Chris *How To Use Homoeopathy*, Element Books 1991 47
Homoeopathy Family Handbook, Thorsons 1986...8
Inglis, Brian Fringe Medicine, Faber & Faber 1964...87
Kohlrausch, A *Handbuch der physikalischen Therapie*, Vol II/I, Stuttgart 1971 72
Latour & Woolgar *Laboratory Life*, Princeton University Press 1986....................85
Lawrence & King *Luna - A Proving*, Helios Pharmacy 1993 65
Lockie, Dr Andrew Family Guide to Homoeopathy, Hamish Hamilton 1990.....87, 88
Mastriciana, Caryl *Gods of the New Age,* Harvest House Publishers, 1985........115
McMillan, Dr S I *None of These Diseases*, Oliphants 1967.....................................70
McNamara, Sheila *Traditional Chinese Medicine*, Hamilton 1995 30
Mintel *Complementary Medicines*, May 1995..1
Nilsson, Lennart *Body Victorious*, Faber 1987...58
Pachter, H *Paracelsus*, Henry Schuman 1951 ....53, 86
Pfeiffer, Dr Samuel *Healing At Any Price*, Word Publications 1988....47, 50, 71, 105
Pocock, Stuart *Clinical Trials*, Wiley 1983 94
Shapter, Dr Thomas *The History of Cholera in Exeter*, S R Publishers 1971.........80
Sherr, Jeremy *Homoeopathic Proving of Chocolate*, Helios 1993...........................67
Sherr, Jeremy *Homoeopathic Proving of Scorpion*, Helios 1990 67
Smith, Trevor *Talking About Homoeopathy*, Insight 1986...................................43, 65

Spiro, Howard *Doctors, Patients, Placebos*, Yale University Press 1986 82

Taylor, A E R *Chemotherapeutic Agents and the Study of Parasites*, Blackwell Publication 26

Telepnef, Boris *The Spiritual Masonry of Johann Starck,* Quatuor Coronati Lodge 2076 (Vol. 41) 1928 ....13, 14

Ullmann, Dana *Homoeopathy - Medicine for the 21st Century*, Thorsons 198941, 44, 79, 83

Vernon, M D *Psychology of Perception*, Penguin 1977 5

Vithoulkas, George *Homoeopathy, Medicine for the New Man*, Thorsons 1985 ..113

Vithoulkas, George *The Science of Homoeopathy*, Thorsons 1986.........................7

Watts, Geoff *Pleasing the Patient*, Faber & Faber 1992...............................24, 70, 77

PRESS & MAGAZINES

BMA News Review April 1996 111

British Medical Journal Vol. 309, 9th July 1994 ....83, 84, 108

Cahoots Magazine. Spring '96 edition 31

Great Guides & Illustrations, Word Publishers 1988...7

Health & Fitness Magazine, April 1995...1

Homoeopathic Development Foundation Information leaflet 58

Levenshulme Hom. Clinic, Manchester Waiting room information 1995...................76

Ultimate Health Magazine, Mail on Sunday, Feb 1996 63

VIDEO COMMENTARIES & LECTURES

Adams, George *in a lecture given to British Congress of Homoeopaths, June 1961 .* 46

Homoeopathy: A Realistic Alternative, a video commentary by Materia Medica Comms. 1993 49

Research Methodology, UMIST course hand-out 1994....................................93, 108

Index

A

Abscess, 28
Aconite, 58
Acris tinctura, 35
Acupuncture, 71, 73
Aesculapius, 101
Allergy, 50
Antibodies, 56
Arnica Montana, 35
Avogadro, 43

B

Bacteria, 57, 70
Belladonna, 19, 20, 32, 59
Benveniste, Jacques, 88, 89, 90
Bioflavanoids, 63
Bone marrow, 55
Boots the Chemists, 107
Bristol, 107
Bronchitis, 96
Brukenthal, Baron Samuel, 10, 14, 53
Brunswick, 20
BUPA, 109

C

Cagliostro, 12
Calcium, 98, 99
Capsicum, 35
Capsicum Anuum, 35
Cattle, 59
Chamomile, 35
Cholera, 79, 80, 81
Cinchona, 23, 24, 25, 26, 32, 35, 39
Cocculus, 35
Cockroaches, 68
Common cold, 63
Coughs, 59, 75
Cromwell, Oliver, 7, 40
crystal, 65

Crystal, 64
Cullen, Dr, 23, 25, 26

D

Day, Christopher, 97
Demonism, 105
Dermatitis, 96
Descartes, 14
d'Hervilly, Melanie, 103
Digitalis, 32
Distilled water, 42, 43
Dizziness, 62
Doctrine of Signatures, 29, 59
Doctrine of Transference, 28
Drosera, 35
Dynamisation, 48
Dysentery, 30

E

Ebers Papyrus, 29
Elephantiasis, 34
Ernst, 45
Ethanol, 64
Eyebright, 29

F

Faculty of Homoeopathy, 107
Fever, 19, 20, 23, 24, 25, 28, 32, 39, 79, 97, 98, 99
Flintstone, 63, 64, 65
Freemasonry, 10, 11

G

Galileo, 3, 77
Germaine, Count de St., 17
Germanium, 86
Germany, 8, 15, 16, 39, 103, 104
Glasgow, 107
Great Plague of London, 29
Gunpowder, 61

H

Hahnemann, Samuel, 7, 8, 9, 10, 14, 15, 19, 20, 21, 22, 23, 24, 25, 26, 27, 32, 33, 34, 35, 36, 37, 38, 39, 40, 41, 42, 44, 45, 48, 50, 51, 52, 53, 54, 59, 60, 65, 66, 67, 74, 80, 85, 88, 100, 101, 102, 103, 104, 106
Hartmann, Franz, 34
Headaches, 62, 64
Heartburn, 71
Heartsease, 29
Hegel, 14
Heine, 45
Herbalism, 5
Herbs, 5, 28, 39
Hermannstadt, 10, 14
Hippocrates, 28, 29
Holism, 1
Holmes, Oliver Wendell, 18
Hospital of Tropical Diseases, 25

I

Ignatia, 35
Immune system, 55, 62, 63
Insomnia, 64
Iridology, 116

J

Jenner, Edward, 18

K

Kidney beans, 30
Kothen, 104
Kothen, Germany, 104

L

Lachesis, 59
Ledum, 59
Leeches, 16, 24, 79
Leibnitz, 14
Leipzig University, 9
Lice, 4, 17, 59

Like cures like, 7, 24, 26, 27, 28, 29, 30, 32, 37, 39, 40, 49, 50
Liverpool, 107
Liverwort, 29
London, 25, 29, 107
Lotus, 30
Luna, 65
Lungwort, 29
Lymph nodes, 57
Lymphocytes, 55, 56

M

Maddox, Dr John, 88
Madgeburg, 10
Malaria, 23, 24, 25, 26, 32
Materia Medica, 99
Medical Control Agency, 107
Meissen, Germany, 8
Mercaptan, 48, 87
Mercury, 37, 61, 79, 80
Montague, Lady, 18
MORI, 1
Mosquito, 25
Mother tincture, 42, 44

N

National Health Service, 107
Naturopathy, 91, 116
Neon, 86
Nitric acid, 61, 63, 65, 79
Nux vomicaSee Strychnine, 34

O

Onions, 42, 43
Opium, 79, 80
Oxygen, 55, 90
Ozone, 90

P

Paganis, Hugo Von, 13
Palestine, 17
Paracelsus, 29, 52, 53, 59, 65, 86
Paris, 45, 61, 100, 104
Pasqually, 12

About the author

Steven Ransom has spent the last nine years investigating alternative health, and in particular, the wider subject of the New Age Movement. Steven's knowledge and experience in this area has led to a growing number of enquiries from organisations across the U.K. seeking a balanced understanding of the subject. Steven lives in East Sussex, is married with three children, and is currently working for an organisation supporting people with mental health difficulties.

At the time of going to press, enquiries on Steven's seminars and/or related matters can be made to the following addresses:

Steve@quackbusters.freeserve.co.uk
Admin@credence.freeserve.co.uk

or write to

Quackbusters,
Credence Publications,
PO Box 15
Uckfield,
East Sussex
TN22 3WX